COLOR AND CLARITY

ASBC HANDBOOK SERIES

Practical Guides for Beer Quality

COLOR
AND
CLARITY

Charles W. Bamforth

University of California, Davis

AMERICAN SOCIETY OF
Brewing Chemists

Library of Congress Control Number: 2018932214
International Standard Book Numbers:
Print: 978-1-881696-31-5
Mobi eBook: 978-1-881696-32-2

American Society of Brewing Chemists
3340 Pilot Knob Road
St. Paul, Minnesota 55121, U.S.A.

For Luke Charles Firman

This Book and This Series

This is the fourth volume in a six-part series addressing quality issues of beer. There are, of course, a number of books and numerous articles that address such matters. This particular series might be viewed as a set of user manuals, much like the handbook that accompanies your car.

In each book I seek to address individual quality issues from a standpoint of

- the basic underpinning science (without getting too complex and grinding the grist too fine),
- the practicalities of the issue pertaining to brewing and its associated activities,
- quality assurance and quality control parameters, and
- a troubleshooting guide (or key control point summary).

Acknowledgment

I am very grateful to Steve McKinley for his excellent artwork.

Suggestion

For those readers who do not have a fundamental understanding of the science and technology of brewing, I suggest that a basic text on beer brewing be read. There are some suggestions under "Further Reading."

Contents

COLOR AND CLARITY

The Importance and Impact of Beer Clarity and Color

It was my first visit to Australia, many years ago. I ordered my beer—a Coopers Sparkling Ale—at the bar and, having handed over my dollars, I found a table and contentedly started to fill my glass from the bottle. "*Hold on*," I remember thinking to myself, "*this is NQB.*" Not Quite Bright. I made my way back to the counter. "Excuse me," I said, "but I don't think this beer is right." The bartender glowered at me and with a snarl barked, "It's supposed to look like that, you Pommy b******." (All part of the friendly banter between the Aussies and the English, also known as Pommies to those Down Under.)

Lesson learned. This beer is every bit as legitimately cloudy as an authentic hefeweissen. If a beer is supposed to be turbid, then ensure it is exactly that. Not brilliantly sparkling (you will realize the irony in the Coopers branding). Not sludge-like. The same. Every time. We have established that principle already in this series. Quality is achieving the desired product—time in, time out. The dreadful reality is that there are rather too many brewers nowadays who do not get it.

Therefore, we have arrived at an era in which profound turbidity has become a statement. For the longest time I have been taught—and in turn taught others—that most beers (certain ones excluded, e.g., Coopers Sparkling Ale) should rejoice in their clarity. There are plenty of examples of beers in which the unexpected appearance of haze, precipitates, and showers of bits (see chapter 7) has led to crises for companies—and at least in one instance hastened the demise of a very large corporation.

So, what are we to make of the so-called East Coast IPA (or New England IPA) phenomenon? Beers that are profoundly turbid. Some claim that they are nothing more than a reflection of either incompetence or laziness in the brewer in not striving to eliminate the cloud. Others argue that those who insist that brightness is best are merely stamping traditions on those who experiment—and claim that the experiment is a success, because plenty of people are buying these products. One cannot argue with the veracity of this latter statement.

Therefore, I turned to Facebook. I posted the photograph shown in Figure 1-1 with this simple request: "I would appreciate your views. Could you look at the photo and tell me which of the beers you would be most inclined to purchase? Just say Left or Right."

As might be anticipated, plenty of folks could not hold themselves back to a single-word answer. The lack of a head on the beers was a deal breaker for some (we deliberately avoided that as a complication, anticipating that people might be distracted by it). Such respondents often declined to decide and, of course, there were plenty who insisted that, without knowing the intended style, it was impossible to comment. Here is a selection of responses:

- Left but I'm an ex brewer. Depends what they smelled/tasted like in all honesty. Lack of head is worrying.
- Left typically. I do enjoy a Hefe or Wit as well.
- This year Right. Last year Left.
- Left, if I don't know what either is supposed to be. Right if it's intentionally hazy by style, weizen or hoppy IPA and that's what I want.
- Of course, it depends on style, but if they taste the same it has to be left.
- Easy, the left because it requires more skill. For some reason, I find most beer geeks want the right.
- Definitely right. Looks like it's got more flavor.
- Me, left. All my beer-drinking customers right (if it was hazier and looked like orange juice).
- Summer: Left. Spring or Fall: Right.
- Right. Left has admirable clarity but looks kind of watery.
- Strangely, left makes me think "industrial" and right "craft."

Fig. 1-1. Comparing brilliant beer with turbid beer. (Courtesy Isabella Perez—© ASBC)

- I see left as process oriented and diligent at producing bright clean beer, and right as only focusing on flavor and not presentation.
- Yes, of course but these days quite a lot of "craft beer" is hazy, either intentionally or otherwise. Rather than accept it, certain drinkers now seek it out or even demand it.
- Need more info—when it gets right down to it, brewer's intent is a big deal.
- I'll take both but left for lager and right for IPA, wit or kettle sour.
- Whichever one tastes better. Left probably has longer shelf life.

- 5 years ago left but now it's a tossup.
- Can I get a sample? Doesn't matter what it looks like anymore.... How does it taste?
- Right looks like it's going to be more of an experience. I'll go for that.
- The left looks too thin and watery and although the right looks as [if] it has more body, it's still light in color but my brain initially says the one on the right.
- Left. But I would taste the right. Sight directs my brain, but [I] have had a few lovely hoppy milkshakes.
- Left. I enjoy craft beer but not if it's half-finished and "green."
- Both for different reasons. I am more inclined toward the right as I prefer the flavor of unfiltered beer. Humans have been drinking cloudy beer for 7,000 years or so and brilliant beers for 160 or so. There is no right answer if it tastes good!
- The beer on the left appears to be fined or (more likely) filtered. Filtration cannot help but remove some of the long chain sugars, which add complexity and richness to beer. Soooooooooo... I'd want to know more before deciding.
- I'd definitely ask my urologist about the right sample.
- Neither. Left looks like cider, right has an odd head and looks like a horse with a problem.
- The horse on the right is not fit for work.

Tallying the scores of those who did commit to one or the other we ended up with 221 left and 112 right. Eighty-four replies gave neither as a preference: they generally wanted more information. On the basis that they were prepared to countenance turbid beer (albeit many specified hefeweissen or wit), I think the safest conclusion for these people is that it really boils down to style and there is nothing inherently wrong with cloudy beer.

There are those who argue that these unfiltered and unclarified beers actually taste better. If that cloud is due to hop material, then they may have a point. However, there are several unsubstantiated beliefs out there that link the removal of materials that simply do not taste of anything to the better quality of unfiltered beer—see, for instance, the comment on "long chain sugars" above.

My mind wanders back to my time with the Bass Company. Perhaps my favorite beer in the stable was Stones Bitter. This was an ale that originated in Sheffield and was possessed of a gentle yellow color, rather lighter than the rest of our pale ales. There were cask and keg versions, which differed only in what happened to them postfermentation. There was no question in my mind that the version of Stones that was fined with isinglass and served from casks was substantially better than the (still enjoyable) kegged version of the product. I always put this down to one main factor: the level of carbonation. The cask version contained about 2.5 g/L of CO_2, whereas the kegged version contained approximately 4.5 g/L of CO_2. However, of course there were other differences, notably that the kegged version was filtered and flash pasteurized, whereas the cask version of course was not. I wonder: did the additional processing take away a certain *je ne sais quoi* from the ale?

My personal preference (not that it matters one jot) is for bright beers, which in the case of my beloved cask ales means properly fined. Over time, I have come to tolerate beers that are NQB (notably the ones traditionally so intentioned). Nevertheless, I must say that I find an overtly sludgy-looking beer to be unappetizing. It straightway makes me contemplate what the impact will be on my digestive system in the upcoming 24 h.

Therefore, what is the science devoted to deciding what folks make of beer clarity? How important is this aspect of a beer's appearance?

There do not seem to be many such studies reported in the literature. One that I am personally familiar with, because it was performed in my laboratory, was by a master's student, Dylan Clark.

I was approached by a North American brewing company in a year when the barley was tending toward higher protein content. It set them a-wondering about whether they were really trying too hard to achieve stability in their beer and what was the verdict from the public on the clarity of the beer. Could the specifications be relaxed? The way we approached this puzzle was to produce a turbid beer in our pilot brewery, one of the same color as the brand from said company, and then to blend the commercial product and our turbid beer in a range of proportions to arrive at a range of degrees of haziness.

We ended up with four beers of haze values 1.49 (reference beer), 3.01, 3.85, and 4.84 nephelometric turbidity units (NTU) (see chapter 8 for information on measuring turbidity). The four beers would be described as brilliant, almost brilliant, borderline very slightly hazy, and very slightly hazy. Each of the three test beers was compared with the reference beer for appearance alone. How Dylan did this was to make

30 pairs of beers (one control and one of the other beers in each pair) and arrange them in a "train" around an oblong bench (Fig. 1-2). The pairs were randomized, with the reference either to the left or the right in each pair, and there was no particular sequence. The lighting was adjusted to match that actually measured in some bars in Davis, California. People (of which there were 53) were asked to walk around the table and circle the number of the beer in each pair that they deemed was the haziest. Binomial statistics were applied, and the aim was to assess the number of judges able to correctly pick out the hazier beer for each pair nine times out of 10 recorded. We also evaluated those succeeding at the 70% level (Fig. 1-3). If you extrapolate the 95% confidence line to the 100% point on the *y* axis, then you can see that almost everyone should be able to pick out a beer of 6.6 NTU as being hazy.

However, for the purposes of our present discussion, perhaps it is the second part of the study that is most interesting. Ten beers were put in a line (randomized) and judges asked to rank them solely based on their appearance. Six commercial beers that had no relevance to the study were put into the experiment to disguise the intent. The other four beers were the control and that sample adjusted to have three haze levels (3.8, 4.8, and 6.8 NTU). You will recognize that the last of these samples had a value close to that which we determined most people should be able to pick out as being at the high end of very slightly hazy. Forty-two people were asked to arrange the beers in their preferred sequence by appearance, from tastiest to least appealing. They were allowed to declare ties. Then the four beers that we were actually interested in were awarded a ranking of 1 through 4 depending on where in the sequence they were placed. Then we crunched the numbers statistically (Table 1-1). There was no statistically significant difference be-

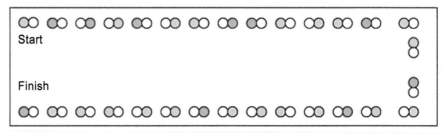

Fig. 1-2. Paired comparisons study. The yellow circles represent the 4.84 NTU beers, orange the 3.85 NTU beers, gray the 3.01 NTU beers, and white the reference beer. NTU = nephelometric turbidity units. (Reproduced, by permission, from Clark and Bamforth [2007])

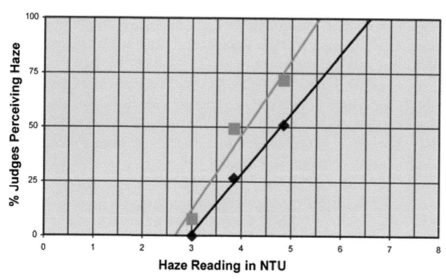

Fig. 1-3. Plots of the results of the paired comparison tests. Plot 1 (large squares) represents the percentages for sensitivity index (d') > 1. Plot 2 (smaller diamonds) represents the percentages for the 95% confidence limit. NTU = nephelometric turbidity units. (Reproduced, by permission, from Clark and Bamforth [2007])

Table 1-1.

Individuals' (42 People Total) Ranking of Beers with Different Clarity Values[a,b]

Beer	Ranked Totals	Average Rank	95% Statistically Different
Clear	96	2.29	From 6.87
3.89 NTU	87.5	2.08	From 6.87
4.80 NTU	103.5	2.46	From 6.87
6.87 NTU	133	3.17	From all others

[a] Courtesy D. T. Clark and C. W. Bamforth—© ASBC.
[b] NTU = nephelometric turbidity units.

tween the positioning of the first three beers. The haziest was decidedly the least preferred, and it was (to remind you) "at the high end of very slightly hazy."

Now, this study was done more than a decade ago. That was before the advent of the overtly turbid products.

What about color?

I described in the volume *Flavor* the experiment we did in coloring up a lager to look like a pale ale and the impact that this had on people's assessment of flavor. It made people describe the flavor in different ways. The color matters. Look again at Figure 1-1. Quite a lot of folks responded that the beer on the left looked like a cider.

One of the extreme examples of a change in beer color came years ago when a major North American company decided they were going to strip all the color out of the beer and serve it "water white." This came around the same time that a prominent cola company tried the same thing. Both products bombed.

What Exactly Is Color?

Chapter 2

You might say color is a state of mind.

Like all our other senses, the color we ascribe to something is the interpretation that our brain puts on what signals our sensing instruments (in this case our eyes) are firing at it. The raw information being supplied to our eyes is electromagnetic radiation (Fig. 2-1).

Electromagnetic radiation is energy emitted as waves by diverse entities. As we look from left to right on the diagram, the waves become closer together—we say that they have a progressively decreasing wavelength. We are all familiar with ultraviolet, short-wavelength light that we cannot see but we can feel if we have spent rather too long sunbathing. It will come as no surprise to those who have experienced sunburn, then, that the shorter the wavelength the higher the energy of that light.[1] At the other extreme are radio waves, which being low energy are not harmful.

The part of the spectrum that interests us in a discussion of color comprises those waves that are in the range 380 to 780 nm (a nano-

---

[1] To get an appreciation of the relationship of wavelength to energy, think about standing with a partner a few yards away and holding a rope between you. If each of you gently start moving your hands up and down, you will start a wave going in the rope. Now if you progressively start moving your hands more and more rapidly the undulations in that rope will increase and the distance between the waves you are producing will become progressively shorter. And the weariness in your arms will tell you that you are expending a lot more energy.

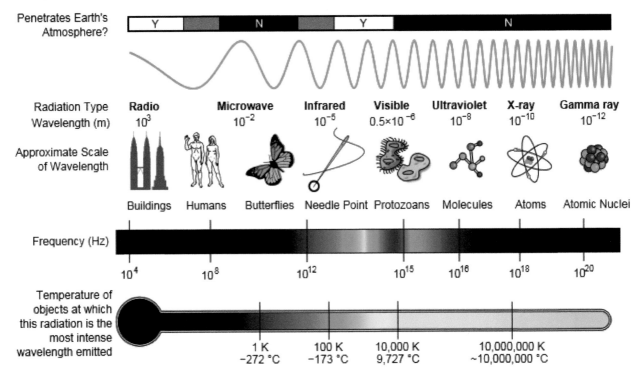

Fig. 2-1. The electromagnetic spectrum. (Data from NASA; figure courtesy Inductiveload—Reproduced according to terms of the GNU Free Documentation License)

meter is one billionth of a meter; Fig. 2-2). At the lower wavelength end we have violet, while at the other end of the visible spectrum is red. We are all familiar with the colors of the rainbow: red, orange, yellow, green, blue, indigo, and violet.

The ultimate light source for us, of course, is the sun. Were we to peer directly at the sun (do not do this!) then we would see white. That is because all of the wavelengths of the visible spectrum are hitting our light receptors, which are entities called rods and cones in the retina of our eyes. When we see a rainbow that is because the different wavelengths of light have been split by a process called refraction, so that we see red on the outer part and violet on the inner part. When white light passes through a prism, the same thing happens, and the light source is split into its component wavelengths.

So how do our eyes register different colors? Let us say we are looking at a New York cab, with its legendary yellow color. It looks yellow to us on a bright, sunny day because the paint that has been used on it absorbs the waves of light at the violet through green end and at the

Color	Wavelength (nm)
Red	620–780
Orange	590–620
Yellow	570–590
Green	495–570
Blue	450–495
Indigo/violet	380–450

Fig. 2-2. Colors of the spectrum. (Courtesy C. W. Bamforth—© ASBC)

orange-red end, but the wavelengths that represent yellow are not removed. Therefore, they bounce off the car and are reflected into our eyes. Now take a flight to London and observe a London taxi. It is black. That is because the paint used on it absorbs all the light. None of it comes back at us. Now jet back over the pond and make your way to Napa Valley, California. Chances are that the stretch limo taking you on your wine tour is white. That is because none of the light is absorbed and all of the wavelengths are coming into your sensing equipment. That is why cricketers wear white on those fabulously warm English summers (that is irony, by the way): white is cooler than other colors because the radiation is being scattered away. It is why you do not wear black in Death Valley, because the fabric is taking all of the wavelengths in.

A glass of clean water looks colorless. That is because none of the wavelengths in the visible range are being absorbed. A glass of milk looks white because not only are none of the wavelengths being absorbed but light is also being scattered, which is not the case with the water.

Of course, if the light source is not "pure white" then this will influence what our eyes detect and therefore brains perceive. If you go into a room where the light bulb is emitting only certain wavelengths—say, red or yellow—then your perception of the colors of objects in that room is not the same as with the original light bulb.

Not only that, the power of the light source is also important. The dimmer the light, the more difficult it is to differentiate color.

Measuring Color

I recall sitting at the back of the room when one of my team at BRF International was giving a talk on color. Suddenly, a voice piped up, "Sorry, pal, but you have been speaking now for 10 minutes and I have not the vaguest idea what you have been talking about."

My sympathies were with both presenter and listener: color is one of the toughest of all things to explain. We made a start in the previous chapter, and now let us continue by talking about how we can put numbers to it, with particular attention to how brewers do it.

Let us start with something called the Lambert–Beer law, named for the Swiss Johann Heinrich Lambert (1728–1777) and the German August Beer (good name, of course, 1825–1863), who obviously did not collaborate. Basically, Lambert said that the thicker the sample the more light is absorbed by it, with Beer adding that the more concentrated a substance is in solution, the more light it will absorb. And so we have the following simple equation:

$$E = \varepsilon c l$$

where E means extinction (another word for absorbance), c indicates concentration, l gives the path length, and ε is the molar extinction coefficient. If you think about it, ε equals E when the concentration is 1 (mol/L, or molar) and the path length is also 1 (cm). So, the higher the ε the more strongly a substance will absorb light.

Now, this law only holds at relatively low concentrations of material, and it of course will not work if the sample being analyzed scatters light in any way. Thus, it generally applies to clear liquids.

Measurements are generally made in a spectrophotometer (Fig. 3-1). This comprises a light source, a prism that allows for the splitting of the light (including ultraviolet) into the component wavelengths, a cell (cuvette) into which the sample is placed, and a detector that compares the amount of light measured with that in the incident beam. The operator can dial in which wavelength of light passes through the cuvette. Alternatively, a spectrophotometer can run a scan on a sample by seeing how much ultraviolet and visible range it absorbs at different wavelengths, and this spectrum is characteristic of a given chemical substance. (We will come across some examples of spectra later in this chapter and in chapter 4.)

Different substances absorb light at different wavelengths. Let us take some examples that we encounter in brewing.

Think about the bitter substances derived from hops. They show strong absorbance, not of light in the visible range (and so they do not influence the color of beer) but rather in the ultraviolet. Therefore, the International Bitterness Unit (IBU) method involves measurements at 275 nm.

Now think about a test that we came across in the previous volume, *Freshness*. This is the indicator time test, which measures the reducing power of a sample by reacting it with 2,6-dichlorophenolindophenol (DCPIP). When it is in an oxidized form it is blue, but if it becomes reduced, it is colorless. This color change can be monitored by measuring the decrease in absorbance at 600 nm.[1]

Therefore, we come to the most frequently used method for measuring color, based on the measurement of the amount of light absorbed at 430 nm. This is encapsulated in standard methods, notably those of the American Society of Brewing Chemists (ASBC, Beer-10A) and the European Brewery Convention (EBC).

In the EBC method the color is calculated as A_{430} (i.e., the amount of light absorbed at 430 nm) multiplied by 25.

---

[1] I know DCPIP well, having done my Ph.D. thesis before most of you were born on an enzyme that we could monitor in this way. To illustrate the point about path length, to lower the absorbance at 600 nm and bring it within the range on the spectrophotometer, instead of using the classic 1 cm path length cuvettes, I used ones with a path length of 0.2 cm, thereby lowering the absorbance fivefold.

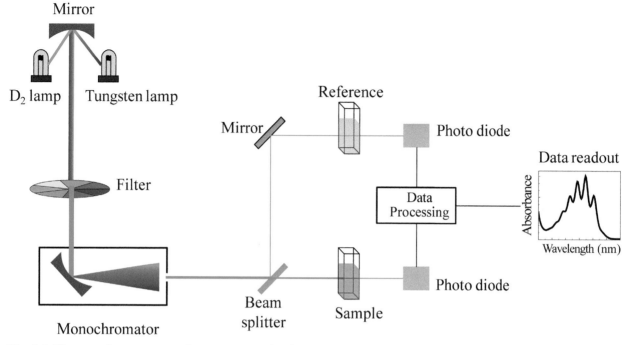

Fig. 3-1. The way that a spectrophotometer works. (Courtesy Sobarwiki)

In the ASBC method the equation is $A_{430} \times 10 \times 1.27$.

Back in the day when the color method was developed it was customary to use cuvettes that were half an inch wide. When most cuvettes used became 1 cm wide an adjustment needed to be made to reflect the shorter path length (see what Lambert discovered all those years ago). There are 1.27 cm in a half inch.

I am sure somebody can explain why the ASBC and EBC elected to use different multipliers (10 and 25, respectively), although I cannot. All that really matters is that if a brewer from Leipzig is talking beer color with someone from Los Angeles they had better know what language they are speaking because a beer like a Bud has a rather higher color value in Germany than it does in the United States, even though it will look the same in both places.

The ASBC method is generally referred to as the standard reference method (SRM). Therefore, the color measurement is °SRM. In the methods involving light absorption it is of course critical that there is minimal light scattering (see above). Thus, it is customary to measure the absorbance value at 700 nm as well, and if its value is less than $0.039 \times A_{430}$ then the beer is satisfactorily "bright." If the value is higher, then the sample needs to be clarified by filtering or centrifugation, mindful of the risk of losing some color in these treatments.

Now, there are problems with this method. Perhaps the experiment that John Smythe and I did back in 2000 suitably illustrates the problem. We took Budweiser, Heineken, Bass, and Guinness (U.S. lager, European lager, ale, and stout, respectively), and we diluted the latter three such that they individually had the same color as the Bud as measured in °SRM. We then showed the beers in pairs to observers and asked them whether there were any significant differences between them. We ensured that differences in foam and clarity were not a factor, and the judges were asked to compare simply based on appearance. The results are shown in Table 3-1. Although the Bud and Heineken were not perceptibly different (the only pair of beers that the judges incorrectly identified as being the same or different was when Bud and Heineken were compared), such was not the case for the Bass and Guinness. In fact, the latter two had a distinct pink coloration.

The reason that observers could see a difference is of course because color is not simply a matter of the intensity of absorbance at a

Table 3-1.

Ability to Differentiate Beers of Identical Color[a]

Test	Beers Compared	Number of Correct Identifications	Significance (2-Tailed)
A	U.S. lager vs. European lager	0/31	$P > 0.999$
B	Stout vs. ale	29/31	$P < 0.001$
C	U.S. lager vs. ale	29/31	$P < 0.001$
D	Stout vs. stout	29/31	$P < 0.001$
E	European lager vs. ale	24/31	$P < 0.001$
F	Stout vs. European lager	31/31	$P < 0.001$
G	U.S. lager vs. U.S. lager	30/31	$P < 0.001$
H	U.S. lager vs. stout	30/31	$P < 0.001$
I	Ale vs. ale	26/31	$P < 0.001$
J	European lager vs. European lager	27/31	$P < 0.001$

[a] Reproduced, by permission, from Smythe and Bamforth (2000).

single wavelength. Rather, it is the extent of absorbance and lack of absorbance of light across the visible spectrum. In fact, back in the day when the (then) Institute of Brewing had its own recommended methods, the color method involved measuring absorbance at 530 nm, because the beers tended to be more amber.

Thus, the color of a beer is going to be influenced by the concentration of color-contributing molecules in the beer (see what August Beer showed), but it will also depend on the precise nature of those substances (and we will come to these in the next chapter). Suffice it to say now that the more intense is the heating used in the production of the specialty malts that are in products like Bass and Guinness, the more complex is the range of color-giving entities in the grist. Figure 3-2 shows the spectra for four beers.

One approach to measuring color that takes account of the perceived color per se involves the use of the Lovibond comparator (Fig. 3-3). Joseph Williams Lovibond (1833–1918) was an English brewer from Greenwich. His inspiration came from sitting in Salisbury Cathedral in Wiltshire and gazing at the stained-glass windows. In

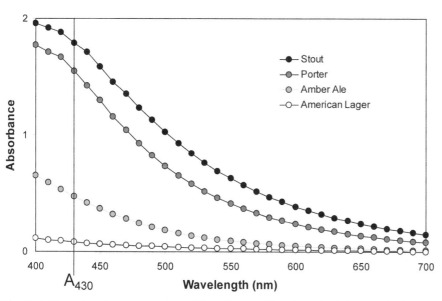

Fig. 3-2. The absorbance spectra of four beers. (Reprinted with permission from Shellhammer, T. H., and Bamforth, C. W. [2008]. Assessing color quality of beer. Pages 192-202 in: Color Quality of Fresh and Processed Foods, ACS Symposium Series 983. C. A. Culver and R. E. Wrolstad, eds. American Chemical Society, Washington, DC. Copyright 2008 American Chemical Society)

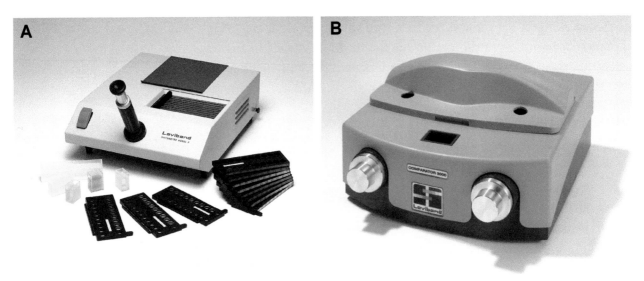

Fig. 3-3. Lovibond instruments for assessing the color of beer in terms of comparison: A, Tintometer; and B, Comparator. (Courtesy Matthew J. Russell, Lovibond—Reproduced by permission)

1885, he launched his company, The Tintometer Ltd., which still exists (http://www.lovibond.com). Fundamentally, a beer is compared with a series of colored disks to arrive at the closest color match.

If you cannot stretch to buying an instrument, then it is always possible to make your color measurements by making comparison to one of the many available color reference standards, such as that to be found at http://cdn.shopify.com/s/files/1/0238/0729/files/srm.PNG?2456.

The downside of such comparison methods as a quantitative tool is that there are varying degrees of color blindness in the population. Thus, we strive for a method that is objective as well as indicative of the precise color of the material that we are testing. And so we turn to the concepts of tristimulus and chromaticity.

You probably have encountered their use before, most likely in a paint store. Say you need to touch up some rotting wood on the outside of the house. How will you know which shade of color you need? If you take a small sample of the wood to the paint store they can put it into their machine and (from the measurements that I am about to explain) can tell you exactly what color you need and mix up the paint accordingly.

Let me illustrate the issues in a bit more detail.

Look at Figure 3-4. If I ask you which of the seven colors the three ovals are on the spectrum, you would say yellow. They are clearly not

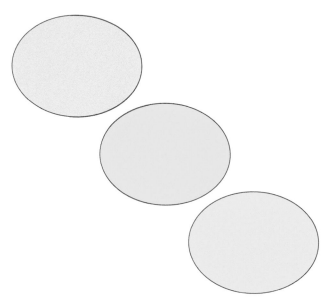

Fig. 3-4. Degrees of yellowness. (Courtesy C. W. Bamforth; Steve McKinley, artist—© ASBC)

blue, red, or green. However, just to say that they are yellow is not enough information. They differ in their dullness versus brightness. They differ in their shade.

Let us turn, then, to the three-dimensional measurement of color, and this is illustrated in Figure 3-5. Let us first take the L axis, with L referring to lightness. Essentially, we are gauging whether the color is relatively light or relatively dark. Totally white has a value of 100, and totally black has a value of 0. The other two key axes are labelled a for the red–green axis and b for the yellow–blue axis. The values range on the a axis from totally green to totally red (–100 is green and 100 is red). On the b axis the spread is from totally yellow (100) to totally blue (–100).[2] Thus, we can place any sample (for example, a beer) in three-dimensional space depending on its relative position on these three axes. We anticipate for most beers that they will show positive values on the a and b axes because they will tend toward the yellow (e.g., a pilsner) or perhaps the red (e.g., an Irish ale). There will of course

---

[2] Note: there are actually two color scales in use, Hunter L, a, b and CIE $L^*a^*b^*$. Be aware of which one you are using. For an overview, see https://support.hunterlab.com/hc/en-us/articles/204137825-Measuring-Color-using-Hunter-L-a-b-versus-CIE-1976-L-a-b-AN-1005b.

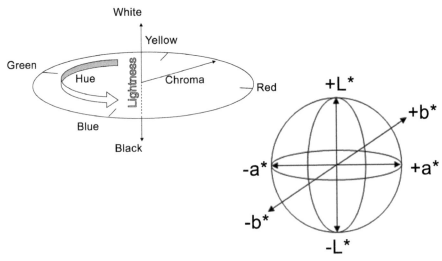

Fig. 3-5. Tristimulus color. Note: there are two different color systems, Hunter and CIE; asterisks indicate CIE *L*a*b** color. (Left, Courtesy T. H. Shellhammer—Reproduced, by permission, from Beer: A Quality Perspective, ed. by C. W. Bamforth, Beer color, by T. H. Shellhammer, pages 213–227, Copyright 2009, Elsevier. Right, Courtesy C. D. Traina and C. W. Bamforth—© ASBC)

be some that are going to score more in the negative region on, say, the *a* axis. Think a Berliner Weiss flavored with waldmeister.

We speak of "hue." This basically is the shade of the color that we perceive, and we are capable of differentiating a thousand of these. So, is a sample lemon yellow, primrose yellow, or gold? Is it cardinal red or ruby red? Is it lime green or olive green? And so on.

Instruments are available that allow this precise assessment of color. Steve Smedley showed that it is actually possible to arrive at the measurement using a simple spectrophotometer and making measurements at five wavelengths: 360, 450, 540, 670, and 760 nm.

The tristimulus method is in the ASBC methods compendium (Beer-10C). Therein you will find a description of making measurements by a dedicated instrument but also the route to the color parameters using a simple spectrophotometer. There is a link on the ASBC site (http://methods.asbcnet.org/eXtras/Tristimulus.xls) that allows the necessary calculations.

The Chemistry of Color

Four main chemical reactions contribute to the color of beer: the Maillard reaction, caramelization, pyrolysis, and the oxidation of polyphenols.

Of these, for most beers it is the Maillard reaction that is the most important, and this occurs primarily during the kilning phase of malting and to a lesser extent during the boiling of wort. This comprises the reacting together of sugars with amino acids in the presence of heat to yield melanoidins. It is a somewhat complex reaction, but suffice it to say here that the extent to which color is developed will depend on how much sugar and amino acid is in the sample of green malt or sweet wort and the length and severity of heating. The colors developed range through the yellows to amber and brown. In terms of malt types, we are talking the pale malts and the lesser intensely heated specialty malts.

Caramelization occurs at high sugar concentrations and intense temperatures, over 120°C. It involves the heat-induced breakdown of sugars and does not involve amino acids. Colors developed tend to be browns and reds. Thus, we are in the range of the caramel and crystal malts.

The extreme of the thermal breakdown of sugars is pyrolysis, at temperatures above 200°C, and the breakdown and burning of the sugars yields black colors. Think chocolate and black malt, as well as roast barley.

Absorbance vs Wavelength

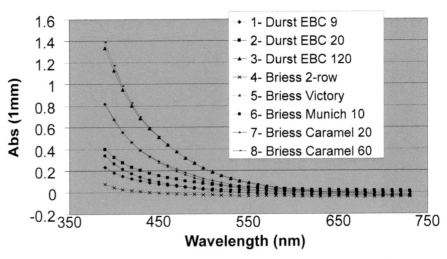

Fig. 4-1. The absorbance spectra of worts made from several malts. (Courtesy C. D. Traina and C. W. Bamforth—© ASBC)

Figure 4-1 shows absorbance spectra for worts produced from some malts in the pale through caramel range and which therefore owe their color to the Maillard reaction and to caramelization. You might compare these with the spectra of beers shown in Figure 3-2. In each case you will see the somewhat simplified nature of the spectra and a dearth of peaks. The inverse of absorption spectra are transmittance spectra, and some of these are shown in Figure 4-2. Again, they might be compared with transmittance spectra for some beers (Fig. 4-3).

Oxidation of polyphenols is the type of reaction that gives the color to sliced apples after they have been in contact with air for a few minutes. It can occur in the presence of high levels of oxygen in wort production or in the finished beer. In mashing, it might be both enzyme-catalyzed and nonenzymic. In the finished beer, it is nonenzymic only. Both the enzymic and nonenzymic reactions mostly do not involve oxygen itself but rather oxygen that has been "activated" by conversion into more energetic form, including peroxide. Figure 4-4 shows the spectrum of an oxidized polyphenol and how it depends on the mode of oxidation. In the case of oxidation stimulated by iron, the peak of maximum absorbance is at a somewhat higher wavelength than we can see occurs in Maillard and caramelization reactions.

%Transmittance vs. Wavelength for Four Worts

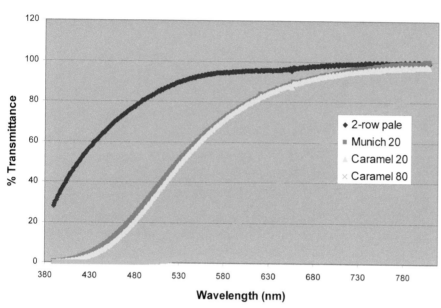

Fig. 4-2. The transmittance spectra of worts made from several malts. (Courtesy C. D. Traina and C. W. Bamforth—© ASBC)

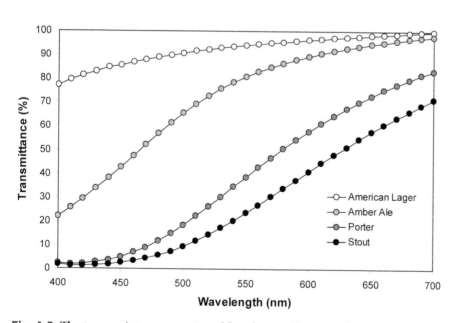

Fig. 4-3. The transmittance spectra of four beers. (Reprinted with permission from Shellhammer, T. H., and Bamforth, C. W. [2008]. Assessing color quality of beer. Pages 192–202 in: Color Quality of Fresh and Processed Foods, ACS Symposium Series 983. C. A. Culver and R. E. Wrolstad, eds. American Chemical Society, Washington, DC. Copyright 2008 American Chemical Society)

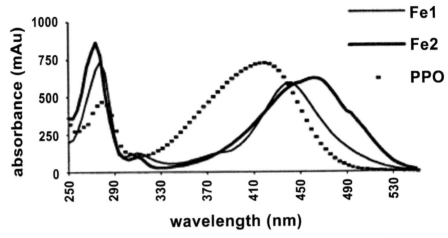

Fig. 4-4. Ultraviolet–visible spectra of the major colored products obtained by iron-catalyzed autoxidation (Fel, Fe2) and enzymatic oxidation (polyphenol oxidase, PPO) of (+)-catechin. (Reprinted with permission from Cheynier, V., Fulcrand, H., Guyot, S., Oszmianski, J., and Moutounet, M. [1995] Reactions of enzymically generated quinones in relation to browning in grape musts and wines. In: Enzymatic Browning and Its Prevention, ACS Symposium Series, volume 600. C. Y. Lee and J. R. Whittaker, eds. Copyright 1995 American Chemical Society)

Factors Affecting Color and How to Control Color

The main source of color in most beers is the malt grist. Adjuncts such as rice, corn, syrups, and sugars for the most part tone down the color. The more intensely heated the malt, the darker and more complex is the color.

There are of course a number of suppliers of malt worldwide. To illustrate the offerings I have turned to just two companies—one based in the United Kingdom (Table 5-1) and the other in the United States (Table 5-2)—that distribute the products of several companies. Table 5-3 furnishes a second comparison of products from different suppliers.

Straightway our attention is focused on the absolute necessity to know what units we are intending to use to measure color. Knowing this, we can straightforwardly calculate how much of a given malt we need to arrive at a target color, assuming that the color delivery will be in proportion to the amount of that malt used in the grist.

Consider this, though. Depending on how a malt is produced (notably barley variety, degree of modification, and precise kilning and roasting regime) we might conceivably have somewhat of a different spectrum from product to product. They might very well have the same color (in whatever units you prefer), but the absolute shade or hue might differ significantly. Furthermore, the products may deliver different perceived flavor even if the color is a precise match.

Table 5-1.

The Muntons Malt Range[a,b]

PRODUCT	COLOUR IoB 515ml mash – EBC units	COLOUR EBC mash – EBC units	COLOUR ASBC mash – Lovibond units	APPROX. EXTRACT L°/ kg (dwt) IoB	APPROX. EXTRACT EBC%	USE	COLOUR/FLAVOUR NOTES
Pale Malts							
Super Pale Ale Malt	2 - 3	2.6	1.4 - 1.9	310	82	IPA, bitter, golden ales, light beers	Our lightest ever pale malt, good for showcasing hops/yeasts.
Maris Otter® Extra Pale Ale Malt (Winter)	2.2 - 3.4	2.8 - 4.4	1.5 - 2	308	81.5	IPA, bitter, golden ales, light beers	Traditional pale malts for top quality warm fermented beers. Slightly darker and 'maltier' than lager malt. The extra pales are similar colour to lager malts but with pale malt qualities. See wort profiles for comparisons.
Propino Extra Pale Ale Malt (Spring)	2.2 - 3.4	2.8 - 4.4	1.5 - 2	310	82	IPA, bitter, golden ales, light beers	
Planet Extra Pale Ale Malt (Spring)	2.2 - 3.4	2.8 - 4.4	1.5 - 2	310	82	IPA, bitter, golden ales, light beers	
Pilsner Malt	2.5 - 3.4	3.2 - 4.4	1.7 - 2	308	81.5	Any cold fermented beers	Cereal, grainy, honey.
Lager Malt	2.8 - 3.4	3.6 - 4.4	1.8 - 2	308	81.5	Any cold fermented beers	Cereal, grainy, higher TN for head retention.
Maris Otter® Pale Ale Malt (Winter)	3.4 - 5.2	4.4 - 6.7	2 - 3	308	81.5	Any warm fermented beers	Traditional pale malts for top quality warm fermented beers. Slightly darker and 'maltier' than lager malt. The extra pales are similar colour to lager malts but with pale malt qualities. See wort profiles for comparisons.
Propino Pale Ale Malt (Spring)	3.4 - 5.2	4.4 - 6.7	2 - 3	310	82	Any warm fermented beers	
Planet Pale Ale Malt (Spring)	3.4 - 5.2	4.4 - 6.7	2 - 3	310	82	Any warm fermented beers	
Venture Pale Ale Malt (Winter)	3.4 - 5.2	4.4 - 6.7	2 - 3	310	82	Any warm fermented beers	
Muntons Pale Ale Malt Blend Maris Otter®/ Propino (50:50)	3.4 - 5.2	4.4 - 6.7	2 - 3	308	81.5	Any warm fermented beers	
Oat Malt	3 - 7	3.8 - 9	1.9 - 3.8	230	60	All beers	Use for mouthfeel and head retention. Gives a sweet characteristic.
Wheat Malt	<5	<6.5	<2.9	315	83.5	Lager, ale, wheat beer	Cereal, nutty.
Mild Malt	5 - 6	6.4 - 7.7	2.9 - 3.3	308	81.5	Bitters, milds, stouts, porters	Sweeter than pale malt. Good to use with high ratios of adjuncts.
Vienna Malt	7 - 12	9 - 15.3	3.8 - 6.2	308	81.5	Lager, continental beers	Inbetween pale and munich, golden and full bodied.
Munich Malt	12 - 20	15.3 - 25.5	6.2 - 10	300	79.3	Any beer	Biscuit, toasted, bready. Gives fuller body and rich malt flavour
Coloured Malts							
Cara Malt 10	8 - 12	10 - 14	5 - 6	300	78	Any Pale beer that needs an increase in body or mouthfeel	Light golden colour with a sweet malty and caramelised flavour.
Cara Malt 30	22 - 43	25 - 49	9 - 19	290	76.5	IPA, bitter, mild, stout, porter, golden	Golden colour, toffee/caramel, sweet.
Crystal Malt 110	95 - 125	147 - 192	41 - 54	285	75	IPA, bitter, mild, stout, porter	Copper/red/amber colour, sweet toffee, biscuit, nutty, malty flavours. These increase as colour increases. Starches are crystalised.
Crystal Malt 150	130 - 170	237 - 305	56 - 73	285	75	IPA, bitter, mild, stout, porter	
Crystal Malt 240	210 - 270	407 - 497	90 - 116	285	75	IPA, bitter, mild, stout, porter	
Crystal Malt 400	360 - 440		154 - 188	277	73	IPA, bitter, mild, stout, porter	
Dark Crystal Rye Malt	200 - 300	226 - 339	86 - 128	277	73	IPA, bitter, mild, stout, porter	Copper/red colour, spicy, sweet toffee, biscuit, nutty, malty flavours.
Roasted Malts							
Amber Malt	40 - 75	45 - 85	17 - 33	270	71	Mild, Bitter, Ales, IPA, brown ale, stout, porter	Straw/golden colour, nutty, light toast.
Brown Malt	140 - 160	158 - 181	60 - 69	250	65.5	Mild, Bitter, Ales, brown ale, stout, porter	Brown/dark amber, coffee, roast, strong toast flavour.

Product						Suitable beers	Description
Light Chocolate Malt	400 - 600	452 - 678	171 - 256	250	65.5	Mild, Bitter, Ales, IPA, brown ale, stout, porter	Dark brown/ruby colour, burnt coffee/chocolate bean, bitter.
Chocolate Malt	900 - 1100	1017 - 1244	384 - 470	250	65.5	Mild, Bitter, Ales, IPA, brown ale, stout, porter	Dark brown/ruby colour, burnt coffee/chocolate bean, bitter.
Black Malt	1200 - 1400	1357 - 1583	512 - 598	230	60	Mild, Bitter, Ales, IPA, brown ale, stout, porter	Dark brown/black colour, burnt toast, charcoal, dry, bitter.
Adjuncts							
Torrefied Wheat	2 - 6	2.6 - 7.7	1.4 - 3.3	280	73.7	All beers	Use for mouthfeel and head retention.
Roast Barley	1050 - 1450	1187 - 1639	448 - 619	230	60	Mild, Bitter, Ales, IPA, brown ale, stout, porter	Dark brown/black colour, burnt toast, charcoal, dry, bitter.
Flaked Malts							
Malted Wheat Flakes	25 - 55	28 - 62	11 - 24	n/a	n/a	All beers	Use for mouthfeel and head retention. Gives a nutty flavour.
Malted Rye Flakes	10 - 40	25.5 - 45	5.3 - 15	n/a	n/a	All beers	Use for mouthfeel and head retention. Gives a spicy/nutty flavour.
Malt Extract							
Cedarex Light Malt Extract	<7	<9	<3.8	310	79.5	Brew extender in any beer	Malt extracts are a liquid form of pale malts. Useful for space saving and reducing spent material disposal. Malt extracts will provide approximately 300L° extract. Best added prior to the boil.
Cedarex Amber Malt Extract	12 - 16	15.3 - 20.4	6.2 - 8.2	310	79.5	IPA, golden, bitter	
Cedarex Medium Malt Extract	24 - 28	27 - 32	9.5 - 11	310	79.5	Bitter, mild, porter	
Wheat Malt Extract	<10	<13	<5.3	310	79.5	Wheat beers, lagers, bitter	
Ntense							
Ntense 200 Liquid	180 - 220	204 - 249	77 - 94	270	71	Suitable additions for any beer	Malted and unmalted barley extract. Gives red/brown colour. Flavours include, liquorice, molasses, plum, roasted notes. Increases mouthfeel. Colour and flavour will increase with the higher numbers. Best added prior to boil.
Ntense 800 Liquid	750 - 850	484 - 961	320 - 363	270	71		
Clarimalt							
Clarimalt XD Liquid	680 - 925	769 - 1045	290 - 395	n/a	n/a	IPA, bitter, mild, porter, stout	Roasted barley malt extract. Improve colour and mouthfeel. The darker liquids have less roasted character. Can be added during the brewing process or in final product.
Clarimalt XD3 Liquid	1200 - 1400	1357 - 1583	512 - 598	n/a	n/a	Bitter, mild, porter, stout	
Clarimalt XD5 Liquid	1600 - 1800	1809 - 2035	683 - 770	n/a	n/a	Bitter, mild, porter, stout	
Dried Malt Extract							
Spraymalt Extra Light	<7	<9	<3.8	370	96	Lager, pilsner, light ales	Spraymalts are a dried malt extract (DME), useful for space saving and reducing spent material disposal. Spraymalts provide approximately 320L° extract, high fermentability, silky mouthfeel. Best added prior to boil. Coloured DME's have had small additions of roast barley malt.
Spraymalt Light	8 - 12	10.2 - 15.3	4 - 6.2	370	96	Brew extender in any beer	
Spraymalt Amber	12 - 14	15.3 - 17.9	6.2 - 7.2	370	96	IPA, bitter, mild, porter, stout	
Spraymalt Medium	24 - 42	27 - 48	9.5 - 16	366	95	IPA, bitter, mild, porter, stout	
Spraymalt Dark	44 - 70	50 - 79	17 - 27	366	95	Mild, porter, stout	
Spraymalt Extra Dark	70 - 120	79 - 136	27 - 45	365	95.5	Mild, porter, stout	
Spraymalt Super Dark	1000 - 1500	1130 - 1696	427 - 640	n/a	n/a	Mild, porter, stout	Dried from pure roast barley malt extract.
Sorghum Extract							
Red Sorgum Extract*	<10	<13	<5.3	300	79.3	Produces gluten free beer. Product not gluten free	Once brewed, all gluten drops out to give a gluten free beer. *Testing needs to be done for every batch to certify for gluten free.*

a Courtesy Nigel Davies, Muntons PLC—Reproduced by permission.
b The IoB 515 mL mash refers to the original method of the (then) Institute of Brewing, in which the small-scale mash was at 515 mL rather than 450 g. Originally, the color in the IoB mash was measured at 530 nm, reflecting the redder hues of British pale ales, but these units are in the EBC format, with measurement at 40 nm.

Table 5-2.

The Malt Range from Brewers Supply Group[a,b]

Color Range (Lovibond)	Supplier and Malt
Pilsner 1.3–2 L.	Castle – Pilsen 2RS 1.5–1.9 L.; Gambrinus – Pilsen Malt 1.3–1.8 L.; Patagonia – Extra Pale 1.5 L.; Simpsons – Pilsner Lager Malt 1.5–1.9 L.; Weyermann – Extra Pale Premium Pilsner 1.2–1.4 L.
Pilsner 1.3–2 L.	Crisp – Europils 1.5–1.9 L.; Rahr – Old World Pils 1.5–2 L.; Simpsons – Finest Lager Malt 1.5–1.9 L.; Weyermann – Barke Pilsner 1.5–2.2 L.; Weyermann – Pilsner 1.5–2.2 L.
Pilsner 1.5–2.3 L.	Patagonia – Pilsner 1.6–2.3 L.; Rahr – Premium Pilsner 1.5–2 L.; Weyermann – Pilsner 1.5–2.2 L.; Weyermann – Barke Pilsner 1.5–2.2 L.
F/M pilsner pale/pils terroir 1.3–2.3 L.	Patagonia – Pilsner 1.6–2.3 L.; Weyermann – Eraclea 1.5–2.2 L.; Weyermann – Floor Malted Bohemian Pilsner 1.6–2.3 L.
Cologne malt (Kolsch) 3.1–3.9 L.	Weyermann Brewing Malt (Type Cologne) 3.1–3.9 L.
F/M pilsner dark 5–8 L.	Weyermann – Floor Malted Bohemian Dark Malt 5.1–8.1 L.
6-Row/diastatic malt 1.3–2.3 L.	Rahr – Standard 6-Row 2.1–2.5 L.; Weyermann – Diastatic Malt 1.5–2.1 L.
Pale malt 1.5–2.1 L.	Simpsons – Low-Color M.O. Extra Pale Ale 1.3–2.1 L.
Pale ale malt 1.5–2.5 L.	Crisp – Plumage Archer 1.8 L.; Gambrinus – Pale Malt 1.5–2.1 L.; MCI – Irish Stout 1.5–2 L.; OiO – Canadian 2-Row 1.6 L.; Simpsons – Golden Promise 1.9–2.4 L.
Pale ale malt 1.7–2.8 L.	Gambrinus – Pale Malt 1.7–2.5 L.; OiO – M.O. Blend, M.O. 1.7–2.4 L.; Simpsons – Finest Pale Ale M.O. 2.1–2.8 L.
Special pale malt 2–2.5 L.	Crisp – Clear Choice 2–2.5 L.
Pale ale malt 1.7–4 L.	Crisp – Chevallier Heritage 2.5–4 L.; Gambrinus – ESB Pale Malt 3–4 L.; MCI – Irish Ale Malt 2–3.5 L.; OiO – English Pale Ale 1.7–2 L.; Rahr – Pale Ale 3–4 L.; Simpsons – Best Pale Ale Malt 2.1–2.8 L.
Pale ale malt 2.5–4 L.	Crisp – Best Ale Malt 2.5–3.5 L.; Weyermann – Pale Ale Malt 2.6–3.4 L.
Pale ale malt 2.5–4 L.	Crisp – Finest M.O. 2.5–4 L.; Gambrinus – ESB Pale Malt 3–4 L.
F/M pale ale malt 2.5–4 L.	Crisp – #19 F/M M.O. 3–4 L.

[a] Courtesy Ian Ward, BSG—Reproduced by permission.
[b] Note here that the color values are declared in Lovibond units. F/M = floor malted.

continued

Table 5-2. continued

The Malt Range from Brewers Supply Group[a,b]

Color Range (Lovibond)	Supplier and Malt
Vienna malt 2.4–6 L.	Castle – Vienna 2.4–3.2 L.; Gambrinus – Vienna 5–6 L.; Patagonia – Vienna 2.4–3.2 L.; Simpsons – Vienna 2.4–4.3 L.; Weyermann – Barke Vienna 2.8–3.9 L.; Weyermann – Vienna 2.8–3.9 L.
Munich malt 5–30 L.	Crisp – Munich 5 L.; Crisp – Munich 20 L.; Gambrinus – Munich 10 L.; Gambrinus – Munich 30 L.; Patagonia – Munich 10–14 L.; Simpsons – Munich 7.3–8.8 L.; Weyermann – Munich Light 5.1–6.9 L.; Weyermann – Munich Dark 8.1–9.9 L.
Rye malt and rye adjuncts	Crisp – Rye Malt 6–10 L.; OiO – Toasted Rye Flakes; Weyermann – Rye Malt 2–4.3 L.
Malted wheat	Crisp – Wheat Malt 1.5–2.5 L.; Gambrinus – Wheat Malt 1.8–2.8 L.; OiO – Canadian Wheat Malt; Rahr – Red Wheat Malt 3–3.5 L.; Weyermann – Wheat Pale 1.7–2.4 L.; Weyermann – Wheat Dark 5.8–7.7 L.
Wheat malt and wheat adjuncts	OiO – Toasted Wheat; Rahr – White Wheat Malt 3–3.5 L.
Wheat adjuncts	Crisp – Torrefied Wheat 2.5–3.5 L.; OiO – Toasted Wheat Flakes
Unmalted wheat	OiO – Raw Wheat; Rahr – Unmalted Wheat 1.5–4 L.

The answer to this conundrum, then, is to specify exactly what supplier(s) you need for a given malt for a specific beer. Hopefully, there will be at least one product that will suit, as it is always a good basic rule to have more than a single supplier for any product that you use.

It is in the selection of the grist materials that the tristimulus approach to measuring color comes into its own.

The question is begged, though, whether even here the technique is overkill. True enough, two different suppliers' crystal malt might deliver slightly different hues when added as the specialty malt source in two different batches of the same beer, let us say an amber ale. However, is the magnitude glaring or relatively subtle? In every likelihood, customers are not going to be making a side-by-side comparison of the two batches, and the magnitude of the difference is likely not noticeable to someone having the two beers on separate drinking occasions. I guess it is something for the purist.

Table 5-3.

Further Comparison of the Color of Different Specialty Malts[a,b]

Malt type	Usage in Beer	Company	Colour ASBC		Colour IoB 450		Colour EBC		Colour IoB 515 mL		Approximate Extracts L°/kg	%
Pilsen	Very low colour for production of pils beers	Dingemans	1.4	1.8	2.3	3.3	2.6	3.6	2.0	2.8	305 - 308	82
		Meussdoerffer	1.4	2	2.3	3.8	2.6	4.1	2.0	3.2	305 - 308	82
		Simpsons	1.4	1.7	2.3	3.0	2.6	3.4	2.0	2.6	305 - 308	82
		Briess	1		1.3		1.5		1.2		305 - 308	82
Pale Ale	Moderate colour for ales and pale ales to contribute a characteristic maltiness	Dingemans	2.7	3.8	5.4	8.1	6.0	8.9	4.7	7.0	305 - 308	82
		Cargill (2 row)	1.5	2.5	2.5	5.0	2.8	5.5	2.2	4.3	305 - 308	82
		Cargill (6 row)	1.5	2.1	2.5	4.0	2.8	4.4	2.2	3.4	305 - 308	82
		Pauls	2.5	3.5	5.0	7.4	5.5	8.1	4.3	6.3	305 - 308	82
		Simpsons									305 - 308	82
		Briess	3.5		7.4		8.1		6.3		305 - 308	
Vienna	Used in specialist beers to impart distinct flavour of nuttiness without stewing sweetness	Meussdoerffer	2	3	3.8	6.2	4.1	6.8	3.2	5.3	300-305	80
		Simpsons	2	4	3.8	8.6	4.1	9.4	3.2	7.4	300-305	80
		Briess	3.5		7.4		8.1		6.3		300-305	80
Munich	Useful in some specialist beers particularly from Germany to impart colour and a distinct fruitiness to the beer due to the stewing on the kiln	Dingemans	4	7	9	16	9	17	7	14	295-300	79
		Meussdoerffer	5	6	11	13	12	15	9	12	295-300	79
		Cargill	8	11	18	25	20	28	16	22	295-300	79
		Briess	10		23		25		20		295-300	79
		Briess	20		47		52		41		295-300	79
		Simpsons	7	9	16	21	17	23	14	18	295-300	79
CARAMELS												
Cara 8	Low colour sweet caramel malt with much less glassiness than crystal. Absence of roast nutty flavours. Improves head retention, body and stability. Can enhance existing flavours	Dingemans	6	9	13	21	15	23	12	18	275-295	75
Car Gold		French and Jupps	7		16		17		14		275-295	75
Cargill Caramel 10		Cargill	8	15	18	35	20	39	16	30	275-295	75
Caramel 10L		Briess	10		23		25		20		275-295	75
Caramalt		Pauls	10	15	23	35	25	39	20	30	275-295	75
		French and Jupps	16		37		41		32		275-295	75
		Simpsons	10	14	23	33	25	36	20	28	275-295	75
		Fawcetts	11	13	25	30	28	33	22	26	275-295	75
Caramalt 15		Bairds	13	17	30	40	33	44	26	34	275-295	75
Cara 20		Dingemans	19	27	45	64	49	70	39	55	275-295	75
Caramel 20L		Briess	20		47		52		41		275-295	75
Cargill Caramel 20		Cargill	15	27	35	64	39	70	30	55	275-295	75
Cargill Caramel 30		Cargill	25	35	59	83	65	92	51	72	275-295	75
Caramalt 33		Bairds	30	37	71	88	78	97	61	76	275-295	75
Cargill Caramel 40		Cargill	35	45	83	107	92	118	72	93	275-295	75
Caramel 40L		Briess	40		95		105		82		275-295	75
Cara 45		Dingemans	40	54	95	129	105	142	82	111	275-295	75
Cargill Caramel 60		Cargill	55	65	131	156	145	171	113	134	275-295	75
Caramel 60L		Briess	60		144		158		124		275-295	75
Cargill Caramel 80		Cargill	70	85	168	204	184	224	145	176	275-295	75
Caramel 80L		Briess	80		192		211		165		275-295	75
Caramel 90L		Briess	90		216		237		186		275-295	75
Caramel 120L		Briess	120		288		317		248		275-295	75
Special B		Dingemans	140	155	336	372	370	410	290	321	275-295	75

[a] Courtesy Nigel Davies, Muntons PLC—Reproduced by permission.
[b] Approximate extracts are for indication only.

The Maillard reaction can also occur in the kettle boil, a further reason why boil times and kettle configurations should not be adjusted.

The second source of color in beer is the oxidation of polyphenols. This is most likely to occur in the brewhouse, especially in sweet wort production, or in the finished beer. It has been suggested that up to 40% of the color of a gently colored North American lager can come from this source. If you are producing a black Irish stout it is an ir-

Table 5-3. continued

Further Comparison of the Color of Different Specialty Malts[a,b]

CRYSTAL											
Pale Crystal	Most widely used of the speciality	Fawcetts	26	35	62	83	68	92	53	72	200-275	65
Light Crystal	malts. Green malt is stewed then	Pauls	35	50	83	119	92	131	72	103	200-275	65
Crystal	dried in the kiln to develop a glassy	Fawcetts	52	60	124	144	137	158	107	124	200-275	65
Medium Crystal	crystallised centre with a distinctive	Pauls	55	65	131	156	145	171	113	134	200-275	65
Crystal 55	redness. At low colour it has sweet	Bairds	50	60	119	144	131	158	103	124	200-275	65
Crystal 65	caramel and at higher colours it has	Bairds	60	70	144	168	158	184	124	145	200-275	65
Crystal 75	burnt fruit notes. As a colourant in	Bairds	70	80	168	192	184	211	145	165	200-275	65
Crystal	an ale grist and known to enhance	French and Jupps	77		185		203		159		200-275	65
Dark Crystal	flavours of other key flavours.	Pauls	65	90	156	216	171	237	134	186	200-275	65
	Improves shelf life, head retention	Fawcetts	86	171	206	411	227	452	178	354	200-275	65
Crystal 100	and flavour stability.	Bairds	95	115	228	276	251	304	196	238	200-275	65
Crystal 150		Bairds	135	165	324	397	357	436	280	342	200-275	65
Extra Dark Crystal		Pauls	120	150	288	360	317	396	248	311	200-275	65
Crystal		Simpsons	53	151	127	363	139	399	109	313	200-275	65
Brown malt	A particular variant whereby	French and Jupps	65		156		171		134		200-275	65
	originally heated with wooden	Simpsons	151		363		399		313		200-275	65
	faggots of hornbeam but now dried	Fawcetts	47	60	112	144	123	158	97	124	200-275	65
	on the kiln. Drier and less sweet											
	than crystal malt of thre same											
	colour. Tends to be used in brown											
	ales and sweet stouts											
AMBER AND LOW ROAST												
Amber	Lightly roasted malt but without	Pauls	15	25	35	59	39	65	30	51	200-275	65
	harsh bitterness of chcocolate malt	French and Jupps	32		76		84		66		200-275	65
	or the like. Generally described as	Bairds	50	70	119	168	131	184	103	145	200-275	65
	having a dry biscuit or baked	Simpsons	17	23	40	54	44	60	34	47	200-275	65
	flavour. Tends to impart a dryness	Fawcetts	39	47	93	112	102	123	80	97	200-275	65
Victory	to beers and enhance colour a little.	Briess	28		66		73		57		200-275	65
Special Roast		Briess	50		119		131		103		200-275	65
ROASTED												
Chocolate	Very dark malt with reasonably	Dingemans	300	380	722	915	794	1006	622	789	150-250	40-60
	bitter flavour used for colour	Pauls	415	490	999	1180	1099	1297	861	1017	150-250	40-60
	adjustment. Generally less harsh	French and Jupps	650		1565		1721		1350		150-250	40-60
	than black malts	Bairds	450	500	1083	1204	1191	1324	934	1038	150-250	40-60
		Simpsons	340		818		900		705		150-250	40-60
		Fawcetts (Chocolate)	400	470	963	1132	1059	1244	830	976	150-250	40-60
		Fawcetts (Pale Choc)	214	256	515	616	566	677	444	531	150-250	40-60
Black Malt	Very dark malt with reasonably	Dingemans	500	600	1204	1445	1324	1589	1038	1246	150-250	40-60
	pronounced bitter, acrid and smoky	Pauls	510	585	1228	1409	1350	1549	1059	1214	150-250	40-60
	flavours. Used for colour	French and Jupps	780		1879		2066		1620		150-250	40-60
	adjustment. Used in porters and	Bairds	500	600	1204	1445	1324	1589	1038	1246	150-250	40-60
	stouts. Generally considered less	Simpsons	472	529	1136	1274	1250	1401	980	1098	150-250	40-60
	acrid than roast barley though this	Fawcetts	520	615	1252	1481	1377	1629	1079	1277	150-250	40-60
	is marginal											
Roasted Barley	Very dark colour with the most	Pauls	600	680	1445	1638	1589	1801	1246	1412	150-250	40-60
	strong burnt, smoky, acrid	French and Jupps	810		1951		2145		1682		150-250	40-60
	bitterness. Gives a distinctive bite	Bairds	500	600	1204	1445	1324	1589	1038	1246	150-250	40-60
	to stouts and similar beers	Simpsons	491		1182		1300		1019		150-250	40-60
		Fawcetts	400	598	963	1440	1059	1584	830	1241	150-250	40-60

relevance. The short answer is that for paler beers this source of color must be considered, and this should focus the attention on controlling the amount of oxidation that occurs in the brewhouse and, indeed, in the beer. Generally speaking, this will be a matter of minimizing oxygen ingress and also the level of oxygen-activating ions (iron, copper, and manganese), a subject given ample attention earlier in this series, in

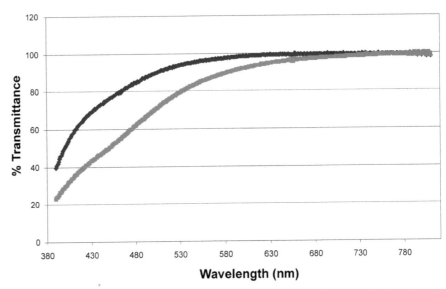

Fig. 5-1. The impact of oxidation on the color of a low-color North American
lager. The oxidized sample was produced by reacting the beer with
hydrogen peroxide in the presence of a peroxidase enzyme. The burgundy-
colored line is the oxidized beer, and the dark blue line is the regular
beer. Note that transmittance indicates the amount of light *not* absorbed
by the sample (in other words, the opposite of absorbance). (Courtesy
C. D. Traina and C. W. Bamforth—© ASBC)

Freshness. An illustration of the impact that oxidation can have on the
color of a pale beer is shown in Figure 5-1.

There is a range of liquid materials that can be used to adjust the
color of beers. These include malt extracts and the caramels. The latter
will modify color without affecting flavor. The former may or may not
affect flavor. If they are simply extracts of specialty malts, then they will
afford both flavor and color to beers. However, it has been suggested
that the color and flavor can be separated based on the size of the different substances (molecular weight). By filtration through membranes
of a certain size cutoff, it is possible to produce low-molecular-weight
fractions that have no color but all the flavor and high-molecular-weight
fractions that have all the color but are devoid of flavor.

Color Troubleshooting Guide Chapter 6

When it comes to controlling the color of beer, the bulk of the job should usually be achieved by controlling the proportion of the appropriately colored grist components in the brew. This presupposes that the color of the various malts being employed maintains a constant relationship with the flavor of that malt. In other words, taking, say, a crystal malt as an example, if that product is made according to a certain regime to a desired color specification, then it will deliver the same flavor every time. Frankly, this is a bold assumption, particularly if one is using comparable malts from different suppliers.

The problem described above is of course going to manifest itself as a flavor issue, it being easier to adjust to a color specification than to a flavor one. In terms of unanticipated color change, then, the number of possible issues is relatively few.

Thus, an unexpectedly high color could be a result of

- Excessive oxidation in wort production
- Excessive heat-induced color formation in the boil
- Excessive oxidation in beer.

An unexpectedly low color could be a result of

- Less than customary oxidation in wort production
- Less than normal heat-induced color formation in the boil

- Less than usual oxidation in beer
- Loss of color through adsorption on surfaces, for example, filter materials.

The solution in all cases is to pay careful attention to all materials and processes and to pursue all steps in a consistent manner.

Types of Turbidity Problems in Beer

For the purposes of this volume I am going to treat the topic of beer clarity from a perspective that unless a beer displays traditional turbidity—for example, a hefeweissen (where the prefix *hefe*, meaning yeast, registers the expected presence of a material causing a lack of clarity)—then it should be *bright*, preferably *brilliant*.

Perhaps a tale from my past illustrates the lengths that I believe one should take to ensure that this happens. In the United Kingdom there is a beer called Worthington White Shield. Back in the day, it belonged to Bass, and it was the beer that was available in the company's research department in Burton-on-Trent. Those were halcyon days when not only was water not forbidden to be drunk in the lab, but neither was beer. White Shield is a bottle-conditioned product. Although I have not scrutinized it recently, back in the day it had a copious amount of sediment, comprising the yeast that was employed to deliver the required carbonation.[1] Devotees of this beer took great pains to pour the beer carefully to ensure that they got a glass of sparklingly clear and foamy White Shield, leaving the yeast in the bottle (although one of

---

[1] Indeed, Katherine Smart (née Wood), in the late 1980s, pursued her Ph.D. thesis in the Burton lab on how to enhance the adhesiveness of this yeast to the bottom of the bottle.

my team, Roy Parsons, ensured that he drank this yeast—good healthy stuff, of course). I do hope that in these days, when clarity seems to be disregarded, this sublime beverage is not being crudely and carelessly slopped into glasses. Having said as much, I know for a fact that another famous beer that is NQB is served in a well-known chain Antipodean-style restaurant in the United States with the question to the purchaser "do you want it rolled?" In other words, would you like it distinctly turbid? All a matter of personal preference.

Let us begin our discussion by considering all the types of clarity problems that can occur in beer.

Precipitates

We will start with precipitates (and I guess the yeast in Worthington White Shield is an example of this, albeit a sediment that is necessary).

One example was reported by Poul Gjertsen of Carlsberg, this being due to the chilling out of very large molecules of β-glucan when a beer was inadvertently frozen. The number one cautionary note from this tale is "do not freeze beer." It is not good for the beer, and it is not good for the integrity of pipes and containers. The second take-home message is to make sure that the β-glucan is broken down properly, in the homogeneous modification of malt and if necessary in sweet wort production. The beer reported in this study was one of higher original extract, and thus possessed of rather more malt per unit volume than one of lower strength. In other words, it had more molecules teetering on the brink of insolubility than in lower gravity beers—and, furthermore, the higher alcohol content would serve to precipitate out the glucan. I cannot be sure, but if Carlsberg were employing centrifuges in the process (for example, to remove yeast), then that would not have helped because the shear forces involved would have served to straighten out the glucan molecules and render them more susceptible to cross-bridging. Herein, then, is a good illustration of how a combination of factors can contrive to produce a perfect storm.

An example close to home for me at Bass was in the alcohol-free beer Barbican. Somehow, the marketing folks had convinced a company in Saudi Arabia to sell this stuff. At first, it was sold in cans, and I rather suspect that it was consumed directly therefrom. (Perhaps herein lies another strategy for those who would be lazy when it comes to clarity: urge the consumer to quaff directly from a container, although I maintain that such a habit is distasteful.) The problem with Barbican arose when the marketing people registered their desire to package the product in a bottle. This is when the complaints arose: a pronounced sediment developed in the bottle, resembling frogspawn. Cutting an already long story short, Roy Cope working in my team found that two materials in the beer were interacting as the cases bounced around on the ship delivering the product to the Middle East, a problem exacerbated because the packages were being unloaded onto a dockside and left there at 50°C (122°F). Those two materials were isinglass finings (regarding which more later), used to help clarify materials in the cold tank in the brewery, and propylene glycol alginate (PGA), employed to enhance foam stability. The lessons to be learned are (1) do not use mutually incompatible processing aids in breweries, (2) minimize physical abuse of beer, and (3) do not expose beer to silly temperatures. We solved the problem by omitting the foam stabilizer.

Bits

Had the Saudis not noticed the sludge in the bottles and gone ahead to pour it out, then the precipitate would have disintegrated to give a bad case of bits. These are discrete, quite sizable particles that are surprisingly often found in beer, although usually only in quite small amounts. You generally do not see them that easily unless you really peer (for example, with the glass of beer held up against a light box of the type I describe in chapter 8). However, what you might see against the otherwise brilliant background are shreds, fibers, or strands suspended and floating in the beer and quite evenly distributed. They have various origins. They could be a result of a small wedge of material that accumulated somewhere, perhaps on a pipe, became dislodged, and disintegrated to give bits. It could be fibers from a sheet filter. It could represent calcium oxalate (see later). Mike Walters reported an example in an Australian beer shipped to Western Europe. The interpretation was that the bits were owing to a combination of arabinoxylans and protein that came out of solution as foam during the lengthy sea passage. A cross-reaction between PGA and papain (see chapter 9) has been reported to cause bits, further emphasizing the truism that it is unwise to employ mutually incompatible process treatments. The most celebrated example of this type of problem arose in the Schlitz company, making me fond of talking about Schlitz Bits. As Martyn Cornell writes,

> Schlitz decided to use another beer stabilizer....Unfortunately, what Schlitz's brewing technicians did not know was that the new anti-haze agent...would react in the bottles and cans with the foam stabiliser they also used, to cause protein to settle out. At its best this protein looked liked tiny white flakes floating in the beer and at its worst it looked like mucus, or "snot," as one observer bluntly called it.

> For months Schlitz kept quiet about the problem...arguing that the haze was not actually physically harmful to drinkers, and in any case not much of the beer would be kept at temperatures at which the haze would form. However, drinkers did complain, sales began to drop and Schlitz had to make a secret recall of 10 million bottles of beer, costing it $1.4 million. (Cornell 2010)

I think the description I used of it being a product that resembled one of the kids' toys that you can invert to give a snowfall scene is more charitable. The reality, though, is that the problem contributed to the death of the company.

Invisible Haze

My old boss at the Brewing Research Foundation, John Hudson, deplored this term, insisting that I come up with an alternative. Hence, *pseudo haze*, but that has never caught on because it prevents people from saying that they have an "invisible haze meter." In this vein, some folks call the problem *instrumental haze*, because it is all to do with how one measures the clarity of beer. The problem arises because very small particles that are not readily distinguishable by the naked eye nonetheless scatter light disproportionately at the 90° angle that was traditionally used to quantify the turbidity of beer (see chapter 8). It is a problem because you must override what your instrumentation is telling you and make a visual judgment. The particles concerned are very small and are not removed by beer filters. Thus, refiltration of beer in the event of a high haze reading caused by these particles will be unsuccessful, a waste of time and money. The problem is resolved if you do not measure haze at a 90° angle of scatter but rather with forward scatter (see the next chapter). This supposes that these tiny particles do not develop into bigger particles that can be seen, but there is scant evidence for this.

One cause of invisible haze is unconverted starchy endosperm in poorly modified malt. Another is cell wall material from yeast, likely rising from stressed yeast subjected to excess agitation, for example, in a centrifuge. A third is glycogen released from yeast. A fourth is the presence of retrograded starch. Retrogradation can occur if the starch molecular chains that are "loosened" up in gelatinization reactions in sweet wort production are allowed to cool and realign before enzymes efficiently break them down.

Visible Haze

When people contemplate clarity ("colloidal") problems, they are usually thinking about an evenly distributed turbidity throughout the beer of whatever degree, ranging from a distinct but "gentle" dullness through to full-blown chicken soup (as I am wont to call it, and I do not consider it to be good for the soul).

We can differentiate this type of issue into *biological* and *nonbiological* haze.

Biological haze is turbidity that is owing to the presence of microorganisms in the beer (and I guess a poorly poured White Shield is one such). Thus, if organisms multiply, they progressively increase the amount of light scattered and can be seen. There is every likelihood that these organisms will also manifest their presence in terms of an impact on the flavor of the beer.

Nonbiological haze is turbidity that is not owing to the growth of living organisms in the beer. I use the term "living" because there is an often-ignored example of nonbiological haze that is caused by dead bacteria. The example I am familiar with arose when we switched from one filter aid to another, one that did not clarify quite so well. As a result, the beer was dull and not the brilliant brightness that we insisted upon. Microscopic examination revealed rod-shaped bacteria. They were as decidedly deceased as John Cleese's parrot but had arisen in a less-than-pristine malthouse, had met their death in the kiln, and had subsequently entered the brew.

There are several rather more common sources of nonbiological haze.

If there is inadequate modification of barley in malting, or β-glucan-rich adjuncts such as barley-based materials or those from rye or oats, then this polysaccharide will be present at increased levels in beer. The problem is exacerbated if there is a shearing of wort or beer, such as with a centrifuge, because there is then an opening up of the glucan molecules that can then interact with one another and agglomerate.

The reality is that the other component of the cell walls, arabinoxylan (pentosan), is much more likely to be a problem. Although there is rather less pentosan than glucan in the barley cell walls, it is not as efficiently degraded during malting and mashing. Consequently, there is likely more pentosan in the finished beer than there is β-glucan, especially if wheat is being used, because the cell walls of wheat contain more pentosan than β-glucan. As with glucan problems, agitation of the liquid, whether in the brewery or in distribution, exacerbates the problem (see the example I mentioned under "bits").

As my students will tell you, I am prone to say that if you have a haze owing to starch in your beer then you are a blithering idiot. I have to bite my lip these days: there are those deliberately adding starch to get the haze they want in their beers. Oh my. Anyway, it is a fact that if starch is not adequately degraded in the mash then some will survive.

We encountered oxalate before, in the context of bits. However, oxalate can contribute to haze per se as well. It is remarkable but true that there is still an inadequate understanding of the factors that influence how much oxalic acid is yielded from the grist, other than that is where it comes from. If it gets into the beer, then it can cause haze and bits. Those bits can cause nucleation and gushing, as we saw in the first volume of this series, *Foam*. Moreover, the oxalate will progressively build up as a deposit on dispense lines, ultimately blocking them. This is called beer stone. The solution is to precipitate the oxalate out in the brewhouse by ensuring that there is sufficient calcium there to convert oxalic acid into the insoluble calcium oxalate.

Another rarely considered clarity problem can arise from can lid lubricants.

The reality is that when people talk about haze their minds straightway turn to proteins and polyphenols. Unquestionably, they are important, but even if you eliminate them as factors then there is still a risk of clarity problems from the materials discussed above. However, proteins and polyphenols have attracted more column inches than the other causes of haze, so it is unavoidable that this will apply here too.

First, we need to define chill and permanent haze. Chill haze is haze that develops when a beer is chilled to 0°C (32°F) but that disappears when the beer is warmed to 20°C (68°F). Permanent haze is present irrespective of the temperature.

Of all the properties that seem to be important for a protein to be involved in haze formation, it seems that the most significant is that it should contain regions rich in proline. (Proline is one of the 20 amino acids that all proteins are constructed from, but technically speaking it is not an amino acid; rather, it is a so-called imino acid, although we do not need to be bogged down in the nuances of that.) We know that the storage proteins in barley, the hordeins, are rich in proline, so it is there that we must look for the key haze-forming entities.

When it comes to the polyphenols, then the chemistry becomes even more complicated. Suffice it to say that a polyphenol becomes capable of forming a chill haze when two of these rather complex molecules (which we can call monomers) link together to become a so-called dimer. These can then bridge between two protein chains, each attaching to a proline-rich region on the adjacent protein chains. In this way, large complexes can be formed that are not soluble (Fig. 7-1). Karl Siebert at Cornell University developed this model to describe chill haze formation.

Imagine these molecules in a beer at room temperature. Both the proteins and polyphenols are gently vibrating. If you chill the beer down to 0°C (32°F), this vibration goes down, they can "find" one another, and the bridges are formed. However, when the beer is warmed back up the relatively weak bridges that hold the molecules together are broken and the insoluble complex "redissolves." Given enough time, stronger, nonreversible bonds develop in the complex, bonds that cannot be overcome by putting energy into the molecules. Now we have permanent haze.

And how do the polyphenols become dimerized? Through oxidation, which is why oxygen is the enemy of clarity as well as flavor—although we will qualify this in chapter 9.

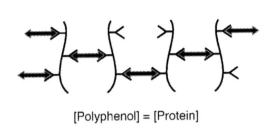

[Polyphenol] = [Protein]

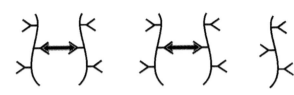

[Polyphenol] < [Protein]

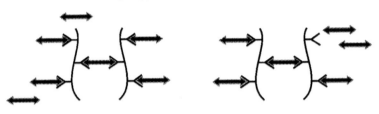

[Polyphenol] > [Protein]

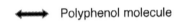 Polyphenol molecule

 Protein molecule with fixed
number of polyphenol binding
sites (i.e. haze-active)

Fig. 7-1. The Siebert model for chill haze. (Reprinted with permission from Siebert, K. J., Troukhanova, N. V., and Lynn, P. Y. [1996] Nature of polyphenol–protein interactions. J. Agric. Food Chem. 44:80–85. Copyright 1996 American Chemical Society)

Measuring and Interpreting Turbidity and Colloidal Stability

The ultimate test of a beer's clarity is simply to look at it. This is best done using a light box of the type illustrated in Figure 8-1. If the edges of the black line appear crisply sharp, then a beer truly is bright.

Brewers, however, always like to have numbers. Thus, we have haze measurements, which historically have been measured in haze meters by assessing the amount of light scattered at 90° to the incident wave. In such devices a light source is beamed into either a glass of the beer or even a bottle. If there are particles in the beer, then they deflect the

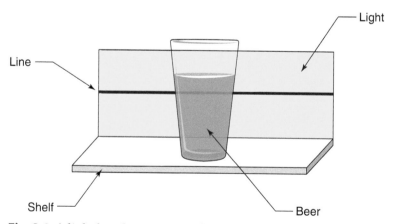

Fig. 8-1. A light box for assessing the clarity of beer. (Courtesy C. W. Bamforth; Steve McKinley, artist—© ASBC)

Table 8-1.

Comparing Haze Measurements by Different Methods[a,b]

Description	NTU	EBC	ASBC
Brilliant	<2	<0.5	<35
Almost brilliant	2–4	0.5–1	35–70
Very slightly hazy	4–8	1–2	70–140
Slightly hazy	8–16	2–4	140–280
Hazy	16–32	4–8	280–550
Very hazy	>32	>8	>550

[a] Courtesy C. W. Bamforth—© ASBC.
[b] NTU = nephelometric turbidity units.

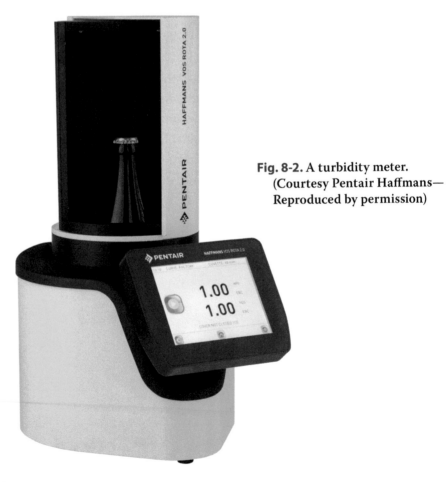

Fig. 8-2. A turbidity meter. (Courtesy Pentair Haffmans— Reproduced by permission)

light, and the extent of this is estimated from measuring the amount of light coming to a sensor set at a right angle to the incident light.

Both the ASBC and the EBC have scales for describing the relative clarity of beer, which is also sometimes quantified as NTU (Table 8-1).

There is a problem with these 90° scatter methods, however. There is a tendency for extremely small particles that cannot be seen with the eye to scatter light disproportionately at right angles. This leads to unacceptably high values in beer that appears bright, so-called invisible haze (see chapter 7). Thus, there has been the development of instruments that do not measure light scatter at 90° but rather at a forward angle of scatter, such as 13 or 30°.

If you have the wherewithal, then it is best to measure at both forward angles and at 90°. Forward scatter is the better indicator of whether the beer is acceptably bright or not, and right angle scatter will give a better indication of total particle counts. The latter tends to be used if you are trying to predict haze in so-called forcing tests.

An example of a haze meter is shown in Figure 8-2. A list of suppliers is given in Table 8-2.

Table 8-2.

Some Suppliers of Turbidity Meters[a]

Company	Website
Haffmans	https://foodandbeverage.pentair.com/en/products/haffmans-turbidity-meter-vos-rota
Lg	http://www.lg-automatic.com/Products/Haze%20Meter/Haze_Meter.html
Hach	https://www.hach.com/tu5
Sigrist	https://www.photometer.com/en/Beer/
Hanna	https://hannainst.com/hi847492-haze-turbidity-meter-for-beer.html
Thermo Scientific	https://www.fishersci.com/us/en/products/I9C8L8O5/turbidity-meters.html
Great River	http://greatriverequipment.com/haze-meters
McNab	http://www.themcnab.com/Products/DLB/Model_DLB_dual_angle_haze_laboratory_instrument.htm

[a] Courtesy C. W. Bamforth—© ASBC.

Forecasting Beer Colloidal Stability

There are two approaches to doing this. The first involves adding an agent that will serve to force out of solution the haze-forming materials that would otherwise appear in the beer in its lifetime in the marketplace. The second involves stressing the beer, either at an elevated temperature or through a cycle of heating and cooling.

The most famous of the forcing tests is the Chapon test. Beer is chilled to −8°C with freezing prevented by the addition of alcohol. After 8 h, chill haze is measured at a scatter angle of 90°. The saturated ammonium sulfate precipitation limit (SASPL) test is a procedure whereby a small sample of beer is titrated with a saturated solution of ammonium sulfate and the haze (90°) measured (Fig. 8-3). The salt molecules compete with the protein molecules for the water needed to dissolve them. If there is not much protein present, then it will take a lot of salt to cause the haze to start to form. However, if there is a lot of haze-forming protein then it will not take much ammonium sulfate to force it out of solution, causing the measured haze to rise. The concentration of salt needed for the haze to start forming is the SASPL value; the lower it is, the less colloidally stable the beer is. An alternative is

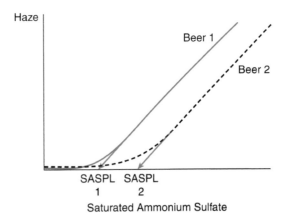

Fig. 8-3. The saturated ammonium sulfate precipitation limit (SASPL) method. Beer 2 needs a greater addition of saturated ammonium sulfate solution to cause a haze, so it contains less haze-forming material. (Courtesy C. W. Bamforth; Steve McKinley, artist—© ASBC)

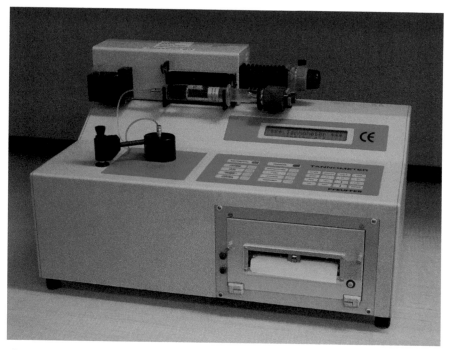

Fig. 8-4. A tannometer. (Courtesy Ken Berg, PQ Corporation—Reproduced by permission)

to titrate with tannic acid, a polyphenol (see chapter 9). The more tannic acid needed to force a haze, the less haze-forming polypeptide is present. Instruments called tannometers are available to do this job (Fig. 8-4).

Siebert et al. (2005) reviewed some of these methods.

An example of a stress test is ASBC Beer-27. Then there is the EBC (1963) method, in which beer is held at 60°C (140°F) for 7 days, cooled to 0°C (32°F) for 24 h, and the haze measured at a 90° angle. There is the Harp method in which the beer is stored for 4 weeks at 37°C (98.6°F) followed by 8 h at 0°C (32°F) and the haze measured at a 90° angle. And there are others, such as the one that holds beer for 24 h at 37°C (98.6°F) and then 24 h at 0°C (32°F) prior to measuring haze at a 90° angle; this supposedly represents the equivalent of 1 month of natural storage. The aim is to see how many cycles the beer can pass through before it becomes visually unacceptable.

It has been suggested that the measurement of polyphenols in beer by using high-performance liquid chromatography, spectrophotometry, or titration with polyvinylpyrrolidone (the monomer of polyvinylpolypyrrolidone [PVPP], see chapter 9) can serve to predict haze. However, results with these techniques have proved mixed.

Measuring Bits

This is most readily achieved by staining the particles with methylene blue. A sample of beer is filtered through paper (2 cm diameter) and the papers exposed to the stain. A series of reference papers with increasing amounts of bits on them can be used for comparison of the level of bits in the sample being tested to allow a semiquantitative judgment of the extent of the problem.

Analyzing Hazes and Other Clarity Problems in Beer

Eventually, turbidity issues will arise in beers (and, again, I am talking here about those products that are supposed not to have such problems). When they happen, we need to have a means to analyze them. Identification of the problem will then enable us to come up with a strategy for preventing the problem from happening again.

We can turn to the methods of the ASBC again for an initial handy-dandy guide, entitled "Beer Inclusions: Common Causes of Elevated Turbidity," which you will find online listed at the end of the Beer Methods section in the ASBC Methods of Analysis. A microscope, a simple centrifuge, and a few dyes are all that is needed. Perusal of the document reveals a few problems not referred to elsewhere in the present book that are worth looking into, namely, dust and liner materials from crown corks, filter aids, and silica gel. (It is ironic that the latter materials used to benefit the clarity of beer can be a problem if used injudiciously, but we have already encountered that in the previous chapter.)

Apart from the methylene blue and Congo red (which stains β-glucan) mentioned in the aforementioned document, there are some other stains that might be employed in support of microscopic analysis (Table 8-3). Remember this, though: all you are staining is what is on the surface. Different materials may be on the inside.

The reality is that you will need a reasonably well-equipped laboratory to analyze hazes, precipitates, and bits. For starters, there is a

Table 8-3.

Some Stains for Analyzing Haze[a]

Material	Stain	Discussion
Carbohydrate	Niagara sky blue 6B	Carbohydrate stains blue
	Thionin	Noncharged polysaccharides such as starch stain violet/blue, whereas acid polysaccharides such as alginates stain rose pink
Starch	Iodine/potassium iodide	Blue indicates the amylose component of starch, and reddish-brown indicates the amylopectin component
β-Glucan	Congo red	Red coloration
Protein	Orange G	Stains protein yellow-brown
	Eosin yellow	Stains protein pink
Yeast cell wall material	Lactophenol blue	Blue coloration

[a] Courtesy C. W. Bamforth—© ASBC.

need for a centrifuge, which will need to reach forces of 10,000–15,000 × g as well as incorporate temperature control allowing 20°C (68°F) for permanent haze or 0°C (32°F) for chill haze. Lower speeds may be sufficient for certain hazes, but still higher g forces of over 100,000 are needed for invisible haze. You might need 5 L of beer, because typically a haze is going to be present in beer at only 2–3 mg/L. The pellets should be washed using an ethanol solution of the same concentration as the beer and the haze recovered by recentrifugation. It should then be dried either overnight in a desiccator or in a 96°C (205°F) oven for 2–4 h. Visible hazes may be collected by filtration (pore size 0.45 μm), but centrifugation is better. So, it is best to turn to a specialist laboratory to do the troubleshooting—and, rather than stain, they will seek to analyze the problem using chemical and enzymic approaches, as I describe in Bamforth (2016).

Assessing Biological Problems

Of course, we may be dealing with a biological haze problem. In the first instance, the microscopic examination referred to above will quickly reveal evidence for molds, yeasts, and bacteria. Thereafter, one may use a wide range of methods for assessing the presence of living organisms. The reality is that if there is a microbial issue serious enough to cause a clarity problem (other of course than organisms that are expected to be in a brew, notably *Saccharomyces cerevisiae* or *S. pastorianus* for most beers and the diversity of organisms to be found in so-called wild beer), then it is likely something that is an even bigger problem in respect to flavor. The "Further Reading" section includes references to useful summaries of microbiological methodology.

Factors Influencing Beer Clarity and Stability: How to Control Them

You might even say that the entire malting and brewing processes are exercises in removing materials that lower the physical stability of beer. Thus, a holistic approach is the most relevant one with regard to enhancing the colloidal shelf life of our products. We will start with raw materials, but it will be recognized that a fundamental feature in our brewery if we are to prevent biological haze centers around hygiene and effective cleaning (see Sidebar 9-1).

Grist Materials

Self-evidently, the more haze-contributing materials present in the grist, the greater the risk. Thus, adjuncts such as rice, corn, high-maltose syrup, and sucrose do not provide any haze-forming entities to the brew. By contrast, higher protein and polyphenol malts deliver more of these substances. β-Glucan and arabinoxylan will come from poorly modified malts, with the former also inputted by grist components such as oats, rye, and torrefied and flaked barley. Arabinoxylan is delivered in higher amounts by wheat-derived grist items.

For some time now, so-called low-proanthocyanidin barleys have been available, from which malts can be produced that lack the haze-forming polyphenols. Some brewers also like such malts because they lead to much less cold break formation and thus brighter worts heading into the fermenter.

Hop Bill

Polyphenols are also delivered into wort and beer from hops. Put simply, the more hop solids used in the brew, either for bittering or for late and dry hopping, the more polyphenols are inputted. If the aim is to deliver a high IBU from a relatively low α-acid hop, you will be adding a lot more polyphenol. By contrast, hop extracts are devoid of polyphenols, so bittering and aroma agents added in this liquid form do not deliver haze-forming potential. Thus, one strategy to eliminate chill haze is to use a combination of low-proanthocyanidin malt and hop extracts.

Malting

Efficient malting is a critical stage for the attendant colloidal stability of the beer. It is necessary that the modification of the barley should be as homogeneous as possible: if there are substantial amounts of grossly undermodified grain left, then the cell wall polysaccharides—and the entrapped protein and starch—will not be degraded, and if not successfully tackled in the mash, they will survive into the wort and beer. Homogenously well-modified malt will contain relatively little problematic β-glucan; however, there will be proportionately greater survival of the arabinoxylan component of the walls, and this is likely to be a bigger problem for the haze stability of beer. Provided the walls are opened up, the proteolytic enzymes should be able to function in digesting the high-molecular-weight protein in the shape of hordein and thereby expose the starch in a form that can be accessed by the starch-degrading enzymes. In malting, this amylolysis efficiently removes the small granules, which are actually problematic for the process and product if they survive. However, the large granules largely survive and will be dealt with in the mash.

Sidebar 9-1. Cleaning and Hygiene

A thorough and all-encompassing cleaning and sanitation program should be in place from start to finish—and this applies no matter what scale you are working on.

This may be automated (so-called cleaning in place [CIP]) or manual. In the latter instance, there may be substantial breaking down of the setup into its component parts, with subsequent scrubbing. In the former, it is mostly conducted without disassembly, although there remains a need to manually attend to some parts of the operation: for example, lauter tun plates will need to be lifted to ensure that the underside is cleaned effectively. On a regular basis, heat exchangers will need to be manually cleaned. In CIP systems, much depends on strategically located and functioning spray balls and pumps.

The soil that we are intent on removing may be trapped in pores or cracks, for example, or may be adsorbed through various forces, both to surfaces and to other types of soil. We are looking for forceful wetting of the soil with attendant scrubbing and chemical and physical interaction followed by removal of the soil from the surface and transfer into the cleaning agent. Thus, significant chemical forces are at play but also mechanical forces. The temperature is significant, as is the duration for which we carry out our cleaning stages.

As well as making sure that the cleaning agents are what they should be and are used in efficient ways, it is also critical that the plant is cleanable. This applies especially in CIP. The cleaning agents must be able to access every square inch of the equipment. There must be no "dead legs" that are not being accessed (e.g., sealed-off side arms of the type illustrated in Figure 9-1). The equipment should be made from materials that are highly chemically compatible, smooth of surface, and of the type that tends to attract less soil. Whether using CIP or manual systems, the appropriate physical forces must be applied. In the latter case, this will be via scrubbing.

It is essential that the water used for cleaning is of top quality, and if stored, this should be in an appropriate way and not for excessive periods.

Primary cleaning agents can be acid, alkali, or neutral and should be employed and handled exactly as per supplier instructions.

The basic four stages of a cleaning operation are water rinse, "detergent" rinse (i.e., the main cleaning stage, which is usually either acid or alkali based), second water rinse, and then sanitation (disinfection). One of the most common agents on a commercial scale is peracetic acid, but others include chlorine-based substances (including chlorine dioxide), iodine-based substances (iodophors), and quaternary ammonium compounds. Alternatively, thermal sanitation can be used if the entire system can be accessed by steam.

Cleanliness is next to godliness. If you get this wrong, quit brewing.

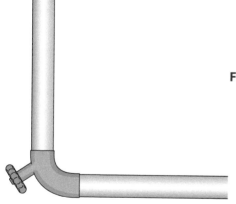

Fig. 9-1. Example of a "dead leg" in a pipeline. Cleaning solutions will tend to flow turbulently through the main pipe but much less so in the sealed-off branch. (Courtesy C. W. Bamforth; Steve McKinley, artist—© ASBC)

Mashing

There are two schools of thought on the matter of low-temperature rests in mashing. The Germanic tradition is to refer to these as proteo-lytic rests, with the insistence that the stage is important for the continuing hydrolysis of proteins begun in the malthouse, such proteins being the hordeins from which the proline-rich haze-forming molecules are derived (see chapter 7). However, another view is that there is little or no proteolysis in mashing. The substantial loss of protein that is witnessed is actually through precipitation (indeed rather more than occurs in wort boiling).

The low-temperature start to mashing is essential for the digestion of any β-glucan that has emerged in the malt or that is present in an adjunct. (Unless, that is, you are prepared to use heat-tolerant β-glucanase, which can be added in at the higher conversion temperature needed for starch. If you are okay with using it—and I personally am on board—then I recommend that you use products that also contain xylanase, or else use an additional xylanase alongside the added β-glucanase.)

At this stage, it is advisable to ensure that you have sufficient calcium present to remove oxalate. One guideline is to add 4.5 times more calcium than the measured oxalic acid—but since I know nobody who measures oxalic acid, I am at a loss regarding how to make this calculation! Another rule of thumb is to ensure a minimum of 80 mg/L of calcium.

Something that we encountered in the previous volumes *Foam* and *Freshness* was the matter of what happens to oxygen in a mash. The diagram shown in Figure 9-2 summarizes this. Put simply, oxygen reacts with the sulfur-rich groups in the so-called gel proteins. By removing hydrogen, the sulfur atoms in adjacent proteins link together, thereby joining the proteins to give sticky gels. This makes for less protein emerging in the wort (i.e., precipitation; see above). The hydrogen peroxide reacts with polyphenols in reactions catalyzed by peroxidase to polymerize the polyphenols, which thereby makes them more ready to react with prolyl-rich polypeptides (see chapter 7). Although this is most prevalent at colder temperatures, we believe that this also happens to an extent in the mash. The result is that there is less polyphenol and protein emerging into the wort and thence into the beer—so, less haze-forming potential. Look at the volume *Freshness* to read my

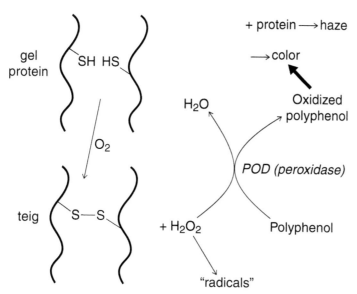

Fig. 9-2. The fate of oxygen in a mash. (Courtesy C. W. Bamforth; Steve McKinley, artist—© ASBC)

thoughts on the relevance of this for flavor stability. Suffice it to say here that I am not advocating for deliberate mash oxidation in the interest of colloidal stability. I am merely suggesting that this may be one of the reasons why the advent of latter-day brewhouses designed to minimize air ingress seemed to coincide with a new wave of haze-stability problems in beer.

These reactions are more prevalent at lower temperatures, so this too may be the real reason why a low-temperature stand works—best call it a "glucanolytic and protein precipitation rest." However, it is of course subsequently essential to have an efficient conversion stage at the higher temperature to deal with the starch that can itself give haze problems.

Wort Separation

Mash-filter-based systems will lead to rather better extraction of everything into wort—the good, the bad, and the ugly. Regarding lauter tuns, apart from avoiding excessive use of the rakes, the main issue is the extent to which the brewer seeks to recover the last traces of extract. As the worts get weaker and weaker they lack buffering potential and, especially when sparge liquor is bicarbonate rich, there will be an increase in pH and attendant increase in the extraction of silicates and polyphenols, both of which cause colloidal instability problems. One approach to counter this is to ensure a sufficiency of calcium in the liquor to counter the bicarbonate, according to the equation for residual alkalinity.

Wort Boiling

The more vigorous the boil, the better the hot break formation, both in terms of quantity and having the structure necessary for good settleability in the whirlpool. Irish moss might be added to further increase the size of the trub, all the better for dropping out in the hot wort receiver. It might be worthwhile to ensure a sufficiency of calcium at this stage, primarily to remove more oxalic acid. There is substantial oxidation of polyphenols in wort boiling, comprising one of the two main pathways for removal of oxygen from the wort, the second of course being the physical driving off of oxygen with the vapor flow.

Wort Cooling

Oxygen has a key role to play in the formation of cold break, through the promotion of protein and polyphenol crosslinks. The tradition in some countries is to remove this break; however, there is a counterargument in that this material promotes the release of carbon dioxide as bubbles in a fermenter, and this in turn leads to the movement of yeast through the fermenter and more efficient fermentations.

Fermentation

Physically unstable materials will be lost with any yeast head in the fermenter, and so technically this may be to the benefit of haze stability. Good yeast management is as important for colloidal stability as it is for foam, flavor, and freshness (see the previous volumes in this series). Stressed and senile yeast that is in poor condition will tend to release carbohydrates and cell-wall materials. One slightly obscure reference has been made to the role that acetaldehyde produced in yeast metabolism can play in cross-linking polyphenols and rendering them in a form capable of cross-linking polypeptides and throwing haze. If this is true, then it would further focus attention on the importance of minimizing acetaldehyde levels in beer (see the volume *Flavor*).

Cold Conditioning

This is usually an important stage for those beers that are destined for filtration and especially for prolonged shelf lives. Two events are at play in a cold tank: the bringing of protein and polyphenol out of solution (namely, chill haze) and the subsequent settling of this material. The latter can be encouraged by the use of isinglass finings and possibly other fining materials (see Sidebar 9-2). The simple reality is that the lower the temperature, the more effective this process is (although freezing is of course to be avoided). Thus, material will emerge at −1°C (30°F) that will not come out of solution at 0°C (32°F), no matter how long the two temperatures are held. Temperature rather than time matters. This is the reason why higher gravity brews can be made more colloidally stable, because they can be taken to lower temperatures without freezing them, thereby bringing out molecules that will not leave the solution at −1°C (30°F).

Filtration

Regarding powder-based filtration systems, diatomaceous earth (kieselguhr) is rather more efficient as a clarifying agent than is perlite, because it contains many holes to trap material, whereas perlite merely acts to adsorb material on its surface (Fig. 9-3). The risk for both is the possible pick-up of iron, which promotes oxidation, including of the polyphenols that can contribute to haze.

Stabilization

For those beers that are destined for lengthy journeys, there is a justification for the use of additional stabilization treatments.

Fundamentally, we can divide these into the ones that remove polyphenol and those that remove protein. It is essential that these materials be used exactly as recommended by the supplier. Some more detail on them is available in the Bamforth (1999) paper listed in "Further Reading" for chapter 7.

The doyen of polyphenol-removing strategies is the use of PVPP. This selectively removes polyphenols and can be used either in the cold tank as a powder addition or as a secondary filtration tool with the PVPP impregnated into filter sheets. The latter can be reused after cleaning with hot sodium hydroxide.

There are two types of silica gel that can be used to remove haze-forming polypeptide. These are the hydrogels and the xerogels, the

Sidebar 9-2. Fining

I have been known to describe an English cask-conditioned ale as being like an angel weeping on my tongue. I consider them the toughest of all beers to deal with successfully, first because of their short shelf life (very soon you can have vinegar) and second because they are traditionally fined, so you really need to know what you are doing if you are not going to have a sludgy and sour pint. Nowadays, this might be no big deal—chapter 1 highlights how broad a range is now acceptable. However, if tradition stands for anything, then it most certainly is.

Traditionally the fining agent of choice is isinglass, a form of collagen extracted from the swim bladders of certain fish. It has a net positive charge at beer pHs and reacts with negatively charged species, notably yeast but also some proteins, to form large complexes that settle out. There is as much art as science in all this. I vividly recall a legendary isinglass salesperson, complete with bowler hat, who would turn up at breweries around the time of the new season's malt, which switchover meant that the fining regimes likely required adjustment. Large tubes would be set up containing the draft ale, and different amounts of finings would be added (e.g., 1 pint per barrel, 2 pints per barrel, and so on). We would look at the way in which the solids dropped out, how long it took, and how compact the sediment was. We would also have a weather eye out for the dreaded "fluffy bottoms," which was a sediment that was relatively unstable, and as the yeast made carbon dioxide, the release caused a lump of the sediment to suddenly puff up and rise. Very undesirable, fluffy bottoms.

The skill was also in making a judicious selection of which negatively charged auxiliary finings to use. These could be materials added in the kettle, notably carrageenan, to increase the size and settleability of hot break material, with the carrageenan reacting with the proteins that have a net positive charge. However, we also used alginate-based finings (some brewers use silicate-based ones) to enhance the removal of such proteins in the finished beer. Mindful that simultaneous addition of isinglass and alginate (or silicate) will lead to the two interacting through negative-to-positive bonding and the attendant removal of both, it is essential that they be added sequentially, with the alginate being added at least 4 h before the isinglass. Silicate-based finings react extremely quickly, and they can be added either before or after the isinglass.

Fig. 9-3. Diatomaceous earth (top) and perlite (bottom) as seen under an electron microscope. (Courtesy Imerys—Reproduced by permission)

latter containing less water. They are claimed not to remove foaming polypeptides and can be used in the cold tank or to replace some of the filter aid in primary filtration.

Tannic acid, which is derived from gallnuts, is a polyphenol with a remarkable ability to react with protein, thereby making enormous precipitates in the cold tank. The latter are a challenge to filter, and there are attendant large losses of beer. For this reason, it is now recommended that this agent should be dosed into beer as it approaches the filter (approximately 5–10 min contact time). With this approach, it is essential to use a coarser grade of diatomaceous earth or to use perlite. It is said that the tannic acid enhances the three-dimensional structure of perlite, thereby enhancing its filtration capabilities.

Papain, a proteolytic enzyme derived from pawpaw, has been used for increasing the colloidal stability of beer longer than any other agent. However, I strongly recommend **against** its use, because it also chews up the foam-stabilizing proteins.

Rather more exciting is the enzyme prolyl endoproteinase, which is specific to the proteins that promote haze and does not damage foam. It is added to the fermenter. Even more exciting than its ability to increase the nonbiological stability of beer it its ability to remove the peptides and proteins that folks with gluten intolerance are sensitive to, and so it is widely used in the production of beers designed for this branch of the populace.

There have been reports of using gelatin to remove other proteins by precipitation, but this is not widely practiced.

Packaging

Primarily it is important that oxygen and ions such as iron, copper, and manganese be at minimum levels in the package, because the oxidation they cause lowers the haze shelf life of beer. Packaging materials (or indeed lines) should not contribute materials that can give clarity problems in beer (e.g., lubricants, oils, and dust).

What About Beers That Are Supposed to Be Turbid?

The reality is that it is more of a challenge to control a finite level of turbidity rather than to prevent a beer from developing turbidity. If that turbidity is owing to yeast, then it is a question of controlling cell counts of the specified yeast strain and ensuring the appropriate extent of flocculation, with the calcium level being a major variable. If it is hop material, then again controlled addition rates are key. If the product is in a can or bottle, then invoke the practice of gentle rolling if it is definitively the case that you want your beer to be uniformly turbid. Alternatively, give the customer the option of having a brighter version by advising on how to pour gently—this presupposing that the insoluble material is not making any direct contribution to the flavor. If we are talking hop material that may be the case. Apart from hop aroma, I am not convinced.

A Turbidity
Troubleshooting Guide

Table 10-1 takes us through a systematic journey to find the underlying cause of whatever clarity problem we have. Many readers will not have a laboratory, although I insist that on all scales of brewing you should have a microscope and be readily able to look at the beer through it, perhaps with the aid of some staining tools (see chapter 8).

Table 10-1.

Turbidity Troubleshooting Guide[a]

Problem	Key Places to Investigate (Priority Order)	What to Do
β-Glucan	Grist	Use homogeneously well-modified malt. Check the modification parameters for the malt (e.g., friability, homogeneity, viscosity, and coarse–fine difference). Seek alternatives to high-β-glucan adjuncts.
	Mashing	Use a low-temperature stand (e.g., 50°C [122°F]) for 20 min to complete glucan degradation. Consider use of heat-tolerant β-glucanase if an infusion mash at starch-conversion temperatures is the only possibility. The performance of such glucanases is enhanced by the coaddition of heat-tolerant xylanases.
	Agitation	Minimize physical forces applied to wort and beer streams (e.g., centrifuges and high-shear flows).
Arabinoxylan	Grist	Use homogeneously well-modified malt (see above). Seek an alternative to wheat-based adjuncts.
	Mashing	Consider use of heat-tolerant endoxylanase.
Starch	Grist	Use homogeneously well-modified malt (see above). This is important to ensure that the starch is freed from entrapment by cell walls and protein.
	Mashing	Use temperatures wisely in relation to the grist materials. Adjuncts with higher starch gelatinization temperatures must be cooked in a cereal cooker, unless they are pregelatinized (torrefied and flaked cereals).
Oxalate	Calcium	Ensure sufficient calcium in the mash and perhaps in the kettle.
Dead bacteria	Grist	Investigate the extent to which there are dead bacteria on the malt. If feasible, work with the maltster on malthouse hygiene.
	Filtration	Ensure filtration strategies (if used) that remove this problem.

[a] Courtesy C. W. Bamforth—© ASBC.

continued

Table 10-1. continued

Turbidity Troubleshooting Guide[a]

Problem	Key Places to Investigate (Priority Order)	What to Do
Protein	Grist	Use malt with the required degree of protein modification. Check the modification parameters for the malt (e.g., friability, homogeneity, soluble nitrogen ratio [also called S/T ratio], and Kolbach index).
	Brewhouse	Consistency in the extent of protein precipitation and removal in sweet wort production. Relevant factors include the amount of oxidation and temperature. Ensure vigorous rolling boil. Possible use of Irish moss (carrageenan). Efficient hot wort stand in the whirlpool: constant time and good settling.
	Conditioning	As cold a temperature as possible without freezing. All the beer should reach the same temperature. Frosted mains all the way to the filter. Possible use of isinglass and auxiliary finings.
	Filtration and stabilization	Filtration systems that afford the greatest possible clarity. Ensure minimum iron pickup. Possibly dosing of tannic acid into beer as it hits the filter. Alternatively, use of silica gel. Alternatively, the addition of prolyl endoproteinase in fermentation. (All agents should be used exactly as per supplier instructions.)
Polyphenol	Grist	Consider use of low-proanthocyanidin malts or malts produced with alkali steeping.
	Hopping	Use high-α-acid bittering hops in the kettle as the primary source of bitterness. Alternatively, use hop extracts (devoid of polyphenols).
	Brewhouse	Keep sweet wort production conditions consistent, with minimum oxygen ingress and precise control of temperature. Avoid "squeezing" out the last bits of extract with prolonged wort collection to lower gravities. Alternatively, maintain a sufficiency of calcium to keep pH low. Consider removing cold break prior to fermentation.
	Filtration and stabilization	Use of polyvinylpolypyrrolidone. Target for a beer of 10°P original extract might be less than 100 ppm after treatment (use ASBC Method Beer-35).

continued

Table 10-1. continued

Turbidity Troubleshooting Guide[a]

Problem	Key Places to Investigate (Priority Order)	What to Do
Living organisms		Hygiene, hygiene, hygiene. See chapter 9.
Fining agents		Use according to supplier instructions—or not at all.
Foam stabilizer		Use according to supplier instructions—or not at all.
Generally		Ensure packaging materials do not furnish haze-inducing material (e.g., can lid lubricants, crown dust, and so on). Ensure as gentle handling as possible of the packaged beer.

Further Reading

The Basics of Malting and Brewing

Bamforth, C. W. (2006) Scientific Principles of Malting and Brewing. American Society of Brewing Chemists, St. Paul, MN.

Hornsey, I. (2013) Brewing. Royal Society of Chemistry, London.

Chapter 1

Clark, D. T., and Bamforth, C. W. (2007) Realistic haze specifications for beer. MBAA Tech. Q. 44:160–163.

Chapter 2

Shellhammer, T. H. (2009) Beer color. In: Beer: A Quality Perspective. C. W. Bamforth, ed. Academic Press, Boston. pp. 213–227.

Further Reading

Chapter 3

De Lange, A. J. (2016) Color. In: Brewing Materials and Processes: A Practical Approach to Beer Excellence. C. W. Bamforth, ed. Academic Press, Boston. pp. 199–249.

Smedley, S. M. (1992) Color determination of beer using tristimulus values. J. Inst. Brew. 98:497–504.

Smythe, J. E., and Bamforth, C. W. (2000) Shortcomings in standard instrumental methods for assessing beer color. J. Am. Soc. Brew. Chem. 58:165–166.

Chapter 4

Shellhammer, T., and Bamforth, C. W. (2008) Assessing color quality of beer. In: Color Quality of Fresh and Processed Foods, ACS Symposium Series 983. C. A. Culver and R. E. Wrolstad, eds. American Chemical Society, Washington, DC. pp. 192–202.

Chapter 5

Comline, P. (2006) Caramel for beer. Brew. Distill. 2(1):17–19.

Smedley, S. (1995) Towards closer color control in the brewery. Brew. Guard. 124(10):42–45.

Chapter 7

Bamforth, C. W. (1999) Beer haze. J. Am. Soc. Brew. Chem. 57:81–90.

Bamforth, C. W. (2011) 125th Anniversary review: The non-biological instability of beer. J. Inst. Brew. 117:488–497.

Connell, M. (2010) How Milwaukee's famous beer became infamous: The fall of Schlitz. Beer Connoisseur. https://www.beerconnoisseur.com/articles/how-milwaukees-famous-beer-became-infamous

Leiper, K. A., and Miedl, M. (2009) Colloidal stability of beer. In: Beer: A Quality Perspective. C. W. Bamforth, ed. Academic Press, Boston. pp. 111–161.

Siebert, K. J., Troukhanova, N. V., and Lynn, P. Y. (1996) Nature of polyphenol–protein interactions. J. Agric. Food Chem. 44:80–85.

Wood, K. A., Quain, D. E., and Hinchliffe, E. (1992) The attachment of brewing yeast to glass. J. Inst. Brew. 98:325–327.

Chapter 8

Bamforth, C. W. (2016) Haze measurement. In: Brewing Materials and Processes: A Practical Approach to Beer Excellence. C. W. Bamforth, ed. Academic Press, Boston. pp. 251–256.

Bokulich, N. A., and Bamforth, C. W., eds. (2017) Brewing Microbiology: Current Research, Omics and Microbial Ecology. Caister Academic Press, Norfolk, U.K.

Buckee, G. K. (1985) Identification of hazes, turbidities, and sediments. In: Proceedings of the European Brewing Convention Congress, Helsinki. pp. 467–474.

Glenister, P. R. (1975) Beer Deposits. J. E. Siebel Sons' Company, Miles Laboratories, Chicago.

Hill, A. E. (2016) Microbiology. In: Brewing Materials and Processes: A Practical Approach to Beer Excellence. C. W. Bamforth, ed. Academic Press, Boston. pp. 291–315.

Morris, T. M. (1987) The relationship between haze and the size of particles in beer. J. Inst. Brew. 93:13–17.

Siebert, K. J., Lynn, P. Y., Clark, D. F., and Hatfield, G. R. (2005) Comparison of methods for assessing colloidal stability of beer. MBAA Tech. Q. 42:7–12.

Storgards, E., Haikara, A., and Juvonen, R. (2006) Brewing control systems: Microbiological analysis. In: Brewing: New Technologies. C. W. Bamforth, ed. Woodhead, Cambridge, U.K. pp. 391–426.

Chapter 9

Freeman, G. (2006) Filtration and stabilization of beer. In: Brewing: New Technologies. C. W. Bamforth, ed. Woodhead, Cambridge, U.K. pp. 275–292.

Further Reading

Knorr, V., Wieser, H., and Koehler, P. (2016) Production of gluten-free beer by peptidase treatment. Eur. Food Res. Technol. 242:1129–1140.

Leather, R. V. (1998) From field to firkin: An integrated approach to beer clarification and quality. J. Inst. Brew. 104:9–18.

Loeffler, D. (2006) Modern brewery sanitation. In: Brewing: New Technologies. C. W. Bamforth, ed. Woodhead, Cambridge, U.K. pp. 308–334.

Miedl, M., and Bamforth, C. W. (2004) The relative importance of temperature and time in the cold conditioning of beer. J. Am. Soc. Brew. Chem. 62:75–78.

Ponton, I. D. (1988) Proanthocyanidin-free malt. Ferment 1(1):33–39.

Roberts, T. R. (2016) Hops. In: Brewing Materials and Processes: A Practical Approach to Beer Excellence. C. W. Bamforth, ed. Academic Press, Boston. pp. 47–75.

For excellent resources on finings and other process aids referred to in this chapter, go to https://www.murphyandson.co.uk and https://bsgcraft.com.

Chapter 10

Lewis, M. J., and Bamforth, C. W. (2006) Essays in Malting and Brewing Science. Springer, New York.

Index

Index

Notes

Notes

Notes

Notes

Notes

Notes

Notes

Notes